BNR - Central

No. 678
$17.95

Modern Communications Switching Systems

By Marvin Hobbs

BNR - Centrad

TAB BOOKS
Blue Ridge Summit, Pa. 17214

FIRST EDITION

FIRST PRINTING—FEBRUARY 1974

Copyright ©1974 by TAB BOOKS

Printed in the United States
of America

Hardbound Edition: International Standard Book No. 0-8306-4678-7

Paperbound Edition: International Standard Book No. 0-8306-3678-1

Library of Congress Card Number: 73-90736

Preface

Some 80 years ago telephone switching began to change from manual to automatic operation, but this change did not come overnight with the invention of the Strowger switch. Decades were required for its full impact to be realized. It is likely that no change since then has been of equal importance in its effect on the structure of telecommunications services until the recent advent of computer-controlled switching techniques. In the years ahead the application of digital central processor techniques (with their inherent software flexibility) to the control of switching elements can be expected to equal or exceed the impact on telecommunications operations created by the historic change from manual to automatic switching systems. The control of switching equipment based on fast operating, high-density digital memories to store readily changed programs marks the beginning of a new era in communications switching.

Unfortunately, the economics of capital investment and the demands for telephone service have made it impossible for this new era to be spawned as rapidly as technology would otherwise permit. Here again, it appears that decades will be required to replace the automatic equipment of an earlier vintage. Nevertheless, certain electronic features are being added to the existing equipment while a modest percentage of telephone lines are being equipped for service by completely new electronic systems. In the U.S. large urban centers are being served first by the new technology due mainly to the fact that it is more adaptable to large numbers of lines. In some countries development has led in the direction of equipment to serve medium-sized communities first. On a worldwide basis, much of the activity in electronic switching for telecommunications is still largely in the developmental or field-trial stages, but most major industrial countries have definite plans to produce and install a significant number of electronic switching systems over the next several years. In some cases military systems have been the first to benefit from the new switching technology because economic considerations have not played as great a role in dictating decisions in this area. The rapidly increasing activity in digital data transmission as well as the benefits derived from converting analog signals to digital form prior to transmission has emphasized the need for digital switching. Since both time-division and message switching techniques lend themselves to this phase of communications, developments in these directions have been accelerated. Digital switching lends itself well to digital transmission networks and will be seen there increasingly in the future. However, it cannot interface economically with existing analog telephone instruments and therefore cannot be expected to penetrate the entire communications hierarchy in the foreseeable future.

Modern Communications Switching Systems might logically encompass only those employing the new techniques of computerized control and digital switching. However, in view of the reality of the situation as stated above one must at least include crossbar and step-by-step systems as well—especially since both of these types, being modernized through the application of electronic control techniques, are likely to serve the public for some time in the future.

This book deals with the basic principles of telecommunications switching techniques ranging from step-by-step and rotary systems to the most modern stored program control electronic systems, as well as time-division switching and those systems used in the switching of digital data. It is intended for use primarily by technical schools and colleges offering courses in telecommunications and related subjects and by engineers and technicians interested in learning more about this field of switching.

For their enthusiastic support and material contributions, I wish to thank the American Telephone and Telegraph Company; Bell Telephone Laboratories, Inc.; GTE Automatic Electric Laboratories, Inc.; The Institute of Electrical and Electronics Engineers, Inc.; The Institution of Electrical Engineers (London); The International Telephone and Telegraph Corp.; L M Ericsson; Nippon Telegraph and Telephone Public Corp.; Philco-Ford; The Plessey Company, Ltd.; The Postoffice Electrical Engineers' Journal; Siemens AG; Stromberg-Carlson Corp.; The University of Essex; and the Western Electric Company.

Contents

The Slow Push for Progress

1

During the 10 years between 1964 and 1974 the number of telephones in the world has doubled. The number of countries with more than a million telephones has risen to 30. During this same period, the number of countries with over 200 annual conversations per person has reached an all-time high. Through cables, land lines, and satellite relays, the U.S. resident has access to more than 98 percent of the world's nearly 300 million telephones. Nineteen of the world's major cities had more than a million telephones each by 1972. In Table 1-1 the top 15 countries in numbers of telephones are listed and in Table 1-2 the 19 cities and urban areas with more than 1,000,000 telephones each are listed in the order of their number of phones.

Table 1-1. Top Telephone Countries

United States	125,142,000
Japan	29,827,936
United Kingdom	16,143,102
West Germany	15,834,827
Russia	11,980,000
Italy	10,321,581
Canada	10,290,305
France	9,546,173
Spain	5,129,501
Sweden	4,679,691
Australia	4,151,622
Netherlands	3,720,817
Switzerland	3,213,065
East Germany	2,165,235
Belgium	2,161,744

In addition to the transmission of voice, the telephone system was called upon increasingly to send and receive data from computers, facsimile equipment, video devices, and other data sources.

Table 1-2. Cities With More Than 1,000,000 Phones

New York City	5,825,460
Los Angeles	4.942,510
Tokyo	4,130,546
London	3,782,828
Chicago	2,358,668
Paris	1,860,875
Moscow	1,625,000
Philadelphia	1,545,192
Osaka	1,450,641
Detroit	1,384,820
Minneapolis-St. Paul	1,306,300
Rome	1,168,672
Buenos Aires	1,115,304
Madrid	1,106,676
Baltimore	1,104,806
Sidney	1,101,168
Montreal	1,030,481
Houston	1,009,193
Milan	1,006,796

TELECOMMUNICATIONS SWITCHING

Since relatively few telephones can provide contact without switching from a multitude of local lines to a much smaller number of trunks between exchanges, the demands for service have not only increased the amount of switching required but have emphasized the need for greater dependability, faster connections, and new conveniences. The importance of switching to telecommunications can be measured to a degree by comparing its costs to that of the other elements of the overall systems. In that regard it represents nearly half the cost of an average telephone call and more than half the cost of a long-distance call. However, with the present-day mix of switching systems—which are predominantly electromechanical—about a fourth the cost of an average call pays for switching equipment and approximately one-fifth goes for operators' salaries. However, the huge capital investment in electromechanical exchanges precludes their replacement for many years especially on a worldwide basis.

Telephone switching is the means by which a communication channel, capable of carrying analog or digital information between two or more subscribers, is established and maintained. Only in the case of private lines is it not required. Any modern telecommunications switching system consists of a great many intricate equipments and components combined into an overall system operating along certain well defined principles. A typical electromechanical automatic switching system contains several master control circuits, each of which consists of some 1500 relays. Such circuits are able to select particular paths and establish a desired connection in less than one second. In doing this, some 700 relays operate and about 10,000 electrical contacts are closed and opened. As an example, a single telephone call from Ann Arbor, Michigan, to downtown Detroit through an electromechanical exchange requires 37,000 relay contacts to make connection. To link any U.S. telephone with any other, the Bell System switching network provides a staggering 2.5 million billion possible connections. The installation of electronic exchanges will reduce the number of relay contact operations considerably—especially in the control portion of the system. But there are still 15 reed relay crosspoints for each subscriber's line in the No. 1 ESS offices. Even when a majority of the subscribers have such electronic switching service, it can be seen that the number of connections to be made for many calls will not be minor.

Present-day telephone-circuit switching equipments are based on either electromechanical techniques (employing crossbar, Strowger, or rotary switches) or electronic techniques (employing either electromechanical or solid-state speech switches and some form of electronic common control). The development of most of these systems has required years of time due largely to the extreme requirements for dependability and reliability. Even a "negligible" amount of downtime of a network cannot be tolerated by the telephone operating companies. There would be a much higher percentage of program-controlled electronic exchanges in use today if the demands for service in the late 1950s had not forced the installation of many crossbar exchanges while the full development of practical electronic exchanges was awaited. Also, at the present time stored-program electronic exchanges are economical only in medium to large central offices and for large private branch exchanges (PABXs). For these reasons, Western Electric produced more electromechanical crossbar switches annually 20 years after the invention of the transistor than ever before; and Japan (a major source of telephone switching systems in the international market) exported only exchanges with crossbar and step-by-step switches during the past decade. Even more surprisingly, Western Electric manufactured more stepping equipment in 1969 and 1970 than ever before and installed the ancient panel system equipment in the world's largest telephone city to cope with the service crisis in New York City.

Switching Systems in Service

Table 1-3 shows the current types of switching systems in service in the U.S., Japan, and the United Kingdom. Note that step-by-step and crossbar systems still switch most of the subscriber lines in these three leading telephone countries.

Table 1-3. Major Exchanges in Service

U.S.	ESTIMATED	JAPAN	ACTUAL
BELL	Jan., 1972	Crossbar C1 (862)	320,000
Panel	4,500,000	Crossbar C2 (645)	450,000
No. 1 Crossbar	6,000,000	Crossbar C3 (179)	250,000
No. 5 Crossbar	17,500,000	Crossbar C45 (434)	2,660,000
Step-by-Step	15,500,000	Crossbar C460 (909)	1,080,000
Step (CDO)	4,000,000	Crossbar C400 (800)	4,810,000
No. 1 and 2 ESS	3,500,000	ESS D10 (1)	200
TOTAL	51,000,000	Total	17,780,200
INDEPENDENT TELCOS			
Step-by-Step	9,000,000	9,570,000	
Crossbar	800,000	UNITED KINGDOM	
Total	9,800,000	Exchange Type	NUMBER
Combined Total	60,800,000	Manual	66
JAPAN		Crossbar	122
	ACTUAL	Electronic	227
	Oct., 1971	Step-by-Step (Strowger)	6172
Manual (2714)	640,000	Total number of local	
Step-by-Step (4317)	7,570,000	lines	10,000,000 approx.

In view of the extensive developmental activity in electronic switching systems and stored program control for telecommunications in all of the leading telephone countries, it may come as somewhat of a surprise to realize that most of the world's telephone lines are still being switched by Strowger, rotary, and crossbar systems. Even in the U.S., where the only significant number of lines are today being served by full-fledged electronic stored-program switching systems, the number of lines still being served by the panel system is of the same order as the number being served by electronic methods. The economics of capital investment and the cost of the new systems undoubtedly has a dominant influence on the continuation of the old switching systems.

Electronic Switching in the U.S.

Starting in 1965 with a single installation of its No. 1 ESS exchange at Succasunna, New Jersey, the Bell System has installed a significant number of stored-program exchanges in large metropolitan centers. Although its No. 1 ESS system has dominated the scene, it has introduced stored-program control in a number of other systems. These include the No. 101 ESS PABX; No. 2 ESS for medium-sized exchanges; Traffic Service Position System No. 1 to assist operators in exchange operations; ADF (No. 1 ESS arranged with data features); AIS (stored-program system that gives the status of non-working numbers); and ETS (electronic translator system for use with toll crossbar exchanges).

At the end of 1972, 320 No. 1 ESS central offices capable of switching about 5,000,000 local lines were in service. In addition to these two-wire exchanges, about 50 4-wire No. 1 ESS systems were in service in the **Autovon** military network. By September, 1972, the in-service installation of many other stored program systems had been made, as shown in Table 1-4.

Table 1-4. Current U.S. Phone-Service Systems

System	Number in Service
No. 101 ESS (PBX and Centrex Service)	250 approx.
ETS—Electronic Translator System	63
TSPS No. 1	56
No. 2 ESS	6
AIS—Automatic Intercept System	2

The Bell System has developed its 1A processor, a high-speed integrated-circuit computer control system, to increase the capacity of local, tandem, and toll electronic exchanges. This processor will also be used with the new time-division toll switching system (No. 4 ESS) which will come into full service within a few years.

Although the percentage of local lines switched by Bell's stored-program ESS exchanges was less than 10 percent in early 1973, an impressive start has been made in the introduction of stored-program control in the U.S.

Electronic Switching Outside the U.S.

Great Britain is the only foreign country which has installed a significant number of electronic exchanges for regular service. But none of these in-service equipments offer stored-program control with the flexibility of readily changeable software. Instead, England's TXE-2 exchange, which is the only one in service at this time, is classified as being programmable in the sense that its operating programs may be changed by the rethreading of wires through ferrite cores. By 1973 nearly 300 of these exchanges, which were designed originally to handle 200 to 2000 local lines, had been placed in service. In the current version of this design, it is extendable up to 4000 local lines. These exchanges will continue to be installed at increasing rates during the next few years.

The U.S. and the United Kingdom are the only countries with in-service electronic exchanges switching a significant number of local lines at this time. Except for ITT's Belgium Metaconta installations, electronic switching installations in the rest of the world were confined to trial exchanges serving less than 10,000 lines each. Extensive development work on stored-program exchanges had been conducted in Japan, Sweden, the Netherlands, France, and Switzerland. In the latter two countries time-division systems were being considered as possible future approaches to comprehensive switching of data, voice, video, and facsimile. Practically every country with a developmental interest in electronic switching spoke of it as the wave of the future and outlined extensive plans to broaden its usage over the next decade. Such plans were given added impetus by the increasing need for digital switching systems to handle high-speed data transmissions and video signals as well as voice and lower speed messages.

Despite all of this interest in electronic switching outside the U.S., it was not yet clear in what form electronic exchanges might ultimately be designed to provide all of the new subscriber services which were being offered by the operating telephone administrations. Most of the services can be provided by crossbar electromechanical exchanges, but with complications and added expense. Electronic systems offered such services with greater economies, but the Bell Systems ESS systems designs appear to be far too expensive for worldwide adaptation. In fact, economics has dictated a hard look at whether stored-program control with full software flexibility is the answer. Some designers favor a wired-logic system, backed by a stored-program processor for the less used facilities and for facility changes.

SUBSCRIBER SERVICES

It has been said that the ultimate goal of telephone switching systems is that every telephone subscriber in the world be able to call any other subscriber without the intervention of a telephone operator. The world's first international direct-dial route was placed in operation in September 1955, between Germany and Switzerland. Although this goal has not yet been realized between many countries, the public has been exposed to many new services beyond the establishment of basic connections between subscribers during the past few years.

Starting with centralized extension service in private branch exchanges in the early 1960s, unique features were offered business subscribers who could afford them in the so-called **Centrex** service packages of the Bell System. Such PABXs provide for direct inward dialing of calls to their extensions and for message accounting of outgoing toll calls for billing purposes, either automatically or by an operator. The latter feature is referred to as identification of outward toll dialing. By furnishing these services, Centrex systems provided the significant advantage of increasing the speed with which incoming calls could be completed to the dialed station extension without operator assistance. The operator workload was reduced, fewer operators were required, and an accounting record of each outgoing call was available for the benefit of the business customer in analyzing the telephone expenses of his various departments.

Crossbar switching equipment has been utilized in Centrex systems throughout the past decade. For instance, in the U.S. one No. 5 crossbar office can serve as a common switching medium for as many as 100 private branch exchanges. Such crossbar equipment is modified to generate and recognize 100 so-called "class of service" marks and 20 rate treatments. The class of service marks identify the PBX and the rate treatments identify the dialing restrictions for each station—assuming that each variation requires a separate rate treatment. The details of Centrex systems, as applied in the U.S. and other countries, will be described more fully in a later chapter.

The introduction of pushbutton telephones has facilitated the expansion of other new subscriber services to include variable abbreviated dialing, call waiting, visible and audible charge information service, add-on, holding, temporary transfer, call transfer on busy, message service, telephone calculating, as well as international direct dialing and various other Centrex functions. Although it is possible to supply most of these services through an electromechanical crossbar switching system, its expansion to include many of these services inevitably leads to complications in circuit and equipment arrangements and excessive increase in the physical size of the installation. The introduction of electronic circuitry and memory into the control section of the exchange offers the best means to introduce the new subscriber services. These can be accommodated more flexibly if stored-program control can be afforded. In that case services can be changed readily by altering software. Even if stored-program control cannot be afforded due to the size of the exchange, electronic componentry is most effective in the translation and memory functions of the exchange.

In addition to providing new subscriber services on a more economical basis, electronic control makes possible highly concentrated maintenance by providing for the replacement of faulty packages rather than requiring the repairing of hardware. Also, only about one-third of the floor space is required for the equipment when compared with the conventional electromechanical crossbar systems due to the use of integrated circuitry and other miniature and subminiature components. Because of its computer capabilities, an electronic switching system is capable of performing store and forward switching—a technique applicable to data handling. Thus, an electronic switching system can serve as a data-switching center by concentrating and distributing various data at different speeds; that is, it can concentrate traffic from terminating devices at low speed and transmit it to a data-processing center at high speed. The process is reversed in the distribution of data. These are some of the reasons why the use of electronic switching in telecommunication systems is bound to grow and why more significant percentages of the total number of local lines will be switched by such equipment in the future.

Subscriber and Exchange Relationships

Within a given urban or city area, the telephone system is characterized by a combination of subscriber subsets (individual telephone instruments), private branch exchanges (PBXs or PABXs), end offices (central offices), tandem offices, and a toll center from which calls are routed to and from subscribers beyond the given city area. These instruments, exchanges, and offices are interconnected as shown in the simplified system of Fig. 1-1. The many subscriber subsets feed to the central offices. In transmitting, the subsets modulate a direct current (usually transmitted from the central office or private exchange) with the acoustic speech message. In receiving, they demodulate the received signal back into its acoustic form. The subsets also generate supervisory signals (on-hook and off-hook) and switching signals (dial pulses or frequencies). There are a variety of subsets in use, ranging from the simplest dial types to pushbuttons. Of course, data modulator-demodulators (modems) are also a form of subset. The subscriber's circuit to the central office provides a two-way path for the message signals and the ringing, switching, and supervisory signals. This circuit is referred to as the subscriber's loop. It is obvious that many calls will be made between subscribers attached to the same central office or private exchange. So, switching of so-called "intraexchange" calls is the first category in any such network.

As soon as subscribers' calls go beyond the local central office, it becomes necessary to transmit to another central office. Connections between exchanges are referred to as trunks. Thus, the difference between a loop and a trunk is seen to be that a loop is permanently associated with a particular subscriber and subset, while a trunk is a common connection between switching offices. As shown in Fig. 1-1, central offices are directly interconnected by paths, referred to as interoffice trunks. It is also seen that central offices are associated with tandem offices, whose purpose is to simplify trunking between these offices. Such an exchange or office serves only as a switching point between central offices and is not directly connected to any individual subscriber lines.

A tandem office effects trunking economies by combining small amounts of interoffice traffic originating in the various central offices and by routing this combined traffic over a common trunk to the required destination, thus eliminating the necessity for inefficient direct interoffice trunk groups. It also provides for the centralization of certain equipment and operations so that each central office need not be burdened

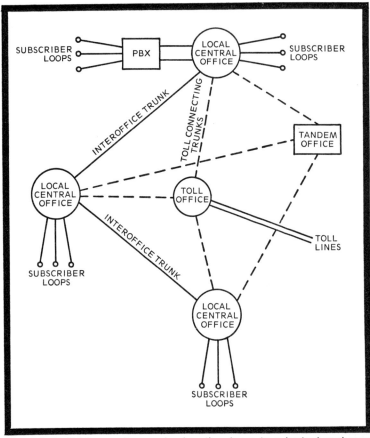

Fig. 1-1. Switching centers and subscriber loops in a typical exchange area.

with facilities which can be shared in common. (Trunks connecting central offices to tandem offices are referred to as tandem trunks.)

Calls between subscribers within a given city area are handled through central and tandem offices; but as soon as the subscriber seeks to go beyond his own urban area, toll offices come into play. Up to this point where signals are transmitted to toll offices, the message and supervisory signals may be handled on a two-wire basis in which the same pair of wires is used for both directions of transmission. However, at the toll office the signals are usually connected to toll trunks by a four-wire terminating set, which splits apart the two directions of transmission so that long-haul transmission may be ac-

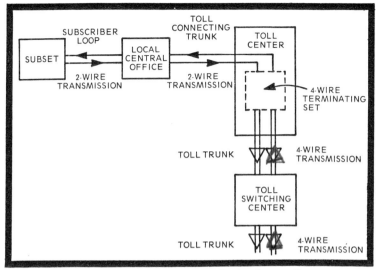

Fig. 1-2. 2-wire and 4-wire methods of operation.

complished on a four-wire basis. The 2- and 4-wire methods of operation in the transmission system are shown in Fig. 1-2. (Connections between toll offices are referred to as intertoll trunks.)

Toll Switching

In the Bell System toll switching plan there are five classes of switching centers, as shown in Fig. 1-3. From the

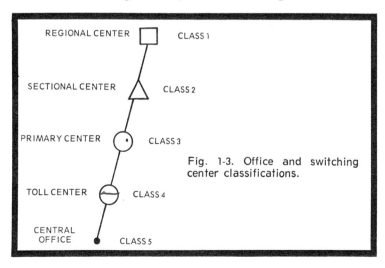

Fig. 1-3. Office and switching center classifications.

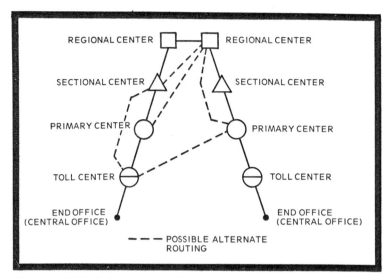

Fig. 1-4. Calls between regional centers may utilize all classes of switching centers.

subscriber's viewpoint, the first class is the central office. Such offices are designated as class 5 offices. The toll center, the next step along the trunking route, is designated as a class 4 office. Following the toll office is the primary center, the sectional center, and the regional center. These offices are designated as class 3, class 2, and class 1, respectively. A majority of toll calls are between central offices associated with the same regional center. In many cases they do not extend to the regional center and in some cases will not involve sectional or primary centers. However, in nationwide toll dialing all centers are involved as shown in Fig. 1-4. Where heavy traffic is expected, an effort is made to provide adequate direct connections between offices; but if overflow traffic should occur, alternate routes must be selected to handle it.

Basic Switching and Traffic Concepts

2

Modern exchanges use either of two basic switching methods: **circuit switching**, in which direct real-time connections are made between subscribers, or **store-and-forward** switching, in which messages are stored and transmitted with variable delays between subscribers. Historically, telephone exchanges have developed around circuit switching methods while teleprinter and Telex transmissions via telegraph channels have evolved around store-and-forward switching. In modern times, circuit switching continues to serve the telephone system and competes with store-and-forward switching for data communication systems. Conventional telephone exchanges employ circuit switching in space-division networks, but time-division switching is beginning to play a more significant role in tandem exchanges, private branch exchanges and in digital transmission systems.

Practically all of the operational concepts of telephone exchange switching have developed around circuit switching principles as embodied in electromechanical devices such as relays, rotary switches, stepping switches, and crossbar switches. It is these concepts and their relationship to telephone traffic that are treated in this chapter. Time-division switching, which also is a category of circuit switching, involves so many new principles and techniques that a complete chapter is devoted to it later. Store-and-forward switching methods in modern applications are largely computer controlled and are related mainly to digital data transmission, so they are also treated separately.

Circuit switching of speech and data paths in electronic exchanges is very little different in principle from that in electromechanical exchanges. It is in the area of common control of the circuit switching that a marked difference exists. All types of exchanges are confronted with traffic engineering problems.

FACTORS IN CENTRAL OFFICE EXCHANGE DESIGN

Central offices provide most of the circuit switching equipment for local lines, which are connected directly with subscribers. Such offices handle from less than 100 lines in small rural communities to well over 10,000 lines in urban areas. However, there is a top limit to the number of local lines which can be handled by one central office beyond which it is necessary to provide additional offices.

For a given number of subscribers, a particular type of switching system is chosen and varied in detail to meet the specific requirements. Engineering of the central office involves selection of the proper quantities of switching equipment, trunks, and related apparatus. To design a central office it is necessary to have a knowledge of the telephone habits of the subscribers—the frequency and duration of their calls as well as daily and seasonal variations in the traffic load as well as contemplated future changes in the number of subscribers.

In a reasonably efficient office it is necessary to provide only for the anticipated maximum number of simultaneous calls, which in practice is always much less than the total number of subscribers. All practical telecommunications switching systems of any size are based on the principle of sharing switching paths by a group of subscribers. In their design, the economies of traffic engineering must be closely coordinated with the capabilities of switching devices and the basic means for controlling them.

TELEPHONE TRAFFIC TERMS AND CONCEPTS

Some knowledge of the more important traffic engineering terms and concepts is necessary to compare and evaluate switching arrangements. The number of connections required in the central office would be equal to half the number of subscribers if all of them wished to talk at the same time. Such a situation is not likely to occur. Normally, only a relatively small percentage of the subscribers use the telephone at a given time; consequently, the switching system is required only to complete connections simultaneously for this number of subscribers. In a typical example, it might be assumed that no more than 10 percent of the subscribers would make simultaneous calls, so the system would be designed to serve this traffic load. Of course, if a greater percentage of subscribers should then try to use this exchange simultaneously, connections would not be established for some calls. These calls would be lost or blocked and certain probability of lost or blocked calls would become a significant factor.

The hour of the day and the season of the year affect the traffic presented to an office. During certain hours of the day the traffic will be heavier than the average hourly level, as shown in Fig. 2-1. Such daily fluctuations will be affected by seasonal variations. Telephone systems are not designed to handle maximum peak loads; rather, they are designed to handle typical busy-hour loads (the period during the day that the most calls occur is defined as the busy hour). During this hour some calls are expected to be blocked. As mentioned, there is a definite **probability** of lost calss during this period, expressed as a decimal, "probability of loss or blockage," such as **P.01**. Such a probability figure means that one call out of a hundred will be blocked during the busy hour. Also, it expresses the grade of service, which will deteriorate when the traffic load is above the busy-hour figure for which the system is designed. Overloads are expected to occur during emergencies and on special occasions.

Traffic Intensity and Grade of Service

For engineering purposes, the characteristics of telephone traffic must be given specific numerical values. Significant

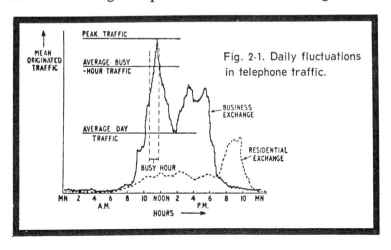

Fig. 2-1. Daily fluctuations in telephone traffic.

terms are the calling rate, the average holding time, and the traffic intensity. The **calling rate**, expressed as calls per hour, is the rate at which the subscriber originates calls or the average number of calls placed by a subscriber during a period of one hour. The **average holding time** is the average duration of one call and may be given in seconds or minutes. For the telephone usage of one or more subscribers making a number of calls, the unit of call-seconds (defined as one call for one second) is used. Measured in hundreds of seconds or hours, other units used are hundred-call-seconds and call-hours.

A measurement essential to the engineering of telephone circuits is the traffic intensity. Measured in erlangs (named after the Danish engineer and mathematician, A.K. Erlang), it represents the circuit usage during an interval of time divided by the time interval. Thus,

Erlangs = call-seconds per second
= hundred call-seconds (CCS or HCS) per 100 seconds
= call-hours per hour.

In any group of observations the total number of circuits found to be busy in all observations divided by the number of observations is equal to the number of erlangs.

Traffic intensity may also be stated in CCS or HCS per hour. Then 1 erlang = 36 CCS ∕ hour or 36 HCS ∕ hour.

In a typical example, a group of 20 subscribers is observed continuously during a 40-minute busy-hour period. During this time they make 30 calls, with a total time for all these calls being 4200 seconds.

Calling rate = average calls per subscriber per hour

$$= 30 \, / \, 20 \times (60 \, / \, 40) = 9 \, / \, 4 = 2.25$$

Average holding time = 4200 ∕ 30 = 140 seconds
Load per subscriber = 2.25 x 140
= 315 call-seconds ∕ hour
= 3.15 HCS ∕ hour
= 3.15 ∕ 36 = 0.0875 call-hours ∕ hour
= 0.0875 erlangs.

Therefore, each subscriber uses an interconnecting circuit for 0.0875 hour during the busy hour, and 20 subscribers would generate a total load of 1.75 erlangs, which means that on the average there would be 1.75 simultaneous calls in existence during the time these observations were made.

Considering Traffic Patterns

In planning new central office installations, the history of groups of subscribers must be considered. For instance, most residential telephones have relatively low calling rates and long holding times, while most business telephones have high calling rates and short average holding times. The total average traffic load offered to a central office is determined by adding the erlang load presented by each subscriber. If sufficient switching equipment is not provided to handle the average traffic loads, too many lost calls may result during temporary peak loads. In a typical case 32 trunks carrying a 20-erlang load will provide a grade of service of P.01, but 36 trunks carrying the same load can provide a grade of service of P.001 (only one call lost in a thousand). However, the 32 trunks operate more efficiently at 63 percent compared with 56 percent for the 36 trunks.

CONNECTING CIRCUITS

In any communications switching system connecting circuits are essential. Such circuits provide the means for establishing interconnecting paths for the transmission of messages, but do not necessarily include within themselves the means for controlling their actions. In fact, except for direct control systems, the controlling elements are distinctly separate. Connecting circuits are used where:

(1) a one-to-one connection is established between circuits on both sides of the connecting circuit, as shown in Fig. 2-2;

(2) many circuits on one side of the connecting circuit are connected to a single circuit on the opposite side of the connecting circuit, as shown in Fig. 2-3;

(3) many circuits on one side of the connecting circuit are connected to many circuits on the opposite side of the connecting circuit (Fig. 2-4).

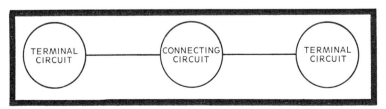

Fig. 2-2. One-to-one connecting circuit.

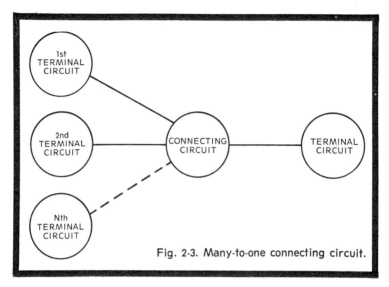

Fig. 2-3. Many-to-one connecting circuit.

In the third case, it is important to recognize that such connecting arrangements are nondirectional. The subscribers on either side may be connected to the subscribers on the opposite side. The functions of connecting N subscriber lines through a somewhat smaller number of connecting circuits thence through trunks to a similar small number of connecting circuits, which in turn connects to N other subscriber lines is referred to as **concentration** and **expansion**.

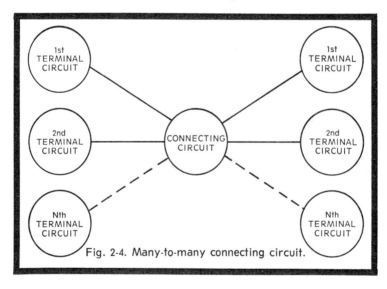

Fig. 2-4. Many-to-many connecting circuit.

Concentration and Expansion

In a switching system the maximum number of simultaneous connections is determined by the number of trunks. The number of subscribers is generally greater than the maximum number of simultaneous connections possible. In practical cases, the desired grade of service and the busy-hour load determines the number of trunks. The traffic must be concentrated in the originating stage of a system so that on the input side of this stage a large number of subscribers can have access to a smaller number of trunks on the output side. The symbol of Fig. 2-5A is used to indicate a concentrating switching stage. In a terminating stage the number of incoming trunks is much less than the number of subscriber lines to be served and an expansion stage is required. The symbol of Fig. 2-5B is used to indicate such an expansion stage. Connections between the concentration and expansion stages are fed through **distribution** stages, which neither concentrate nor expand connections. A basic switching network consists of a concentration stage followed by a distribution stage for the originating connections and a similar distribution stage feeding into an expansion stage for completing the terminating connections (Fig. 2-6).

The functional diagram of Fig. 2-7 illustrates concentration, distribution, and expansion in a simple switching circuit. The 10 subscriber lines on the left side are concentrated to 2 connecting lines; 10 subscriber lines on the right side are served by 2 connecting lines through expansion, and the 2 connecting lines are interconnected by switching to provide distribution. Such a distribution stage is necessary to give each concentration and expansion switch access to all 10

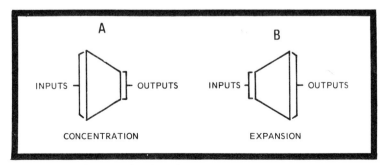

Fig. 2-5. Symbols for switching networks.

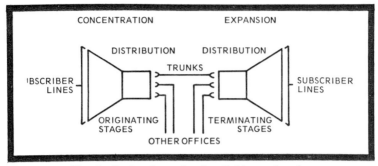

Fig. 2-. Basic elements of switching networks.

subscribers on both sides of the network. Such an elementary switching system would be hard to find in practice, but it illustrates some basic aspects of communications switching. Although there are several ways of showing switching elements in step-by-step, rotary, and crossbar systems, the symbol of Fig. 2-8A is often used to illustrate circuits with any of these systems. The symbol of Fig. 2-8B is also used to show single or multiple input or output switches. When faced in one direction, they represent concentration; when faced in the opposite direction they represent expansion.

Use of the Multiple

An arrangement referred to as a **multiple** is used in connecting circuits to provide the various connections. As

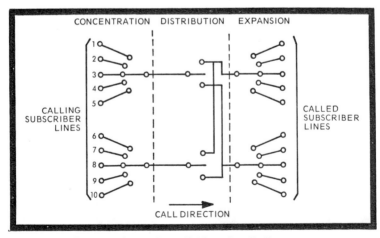

Fig. 2-7. A simple switching circuit diagram.

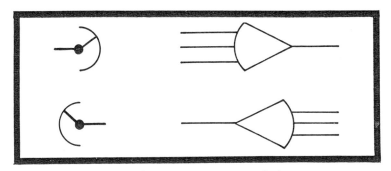

Fig. 2-8. Symbols for switching devices.

shown in Fig. 2-9, any of the circuits (A1, A2, ...) may be connected to a common circuit (Bn) by the operation of relays R1, R2. Such an arrangement is called a multiple because all of the relays have corresponding contact terminals on one side multiplied to a set of common leads (Bn). For simplicity, only one contact is shown on each relay. Of course, several contacts could be provided. Figure 2-10 shows an extension of the multiple principle to provide many interconnections. Such an arrangement may be seen as a crosspoint array in which each circuit on one side is associated with a row of connecting relays, while each circuit on the other side is associated with a column of connecting relays. It follows that such an array may contain reed relays or the switching elements of a crossbar

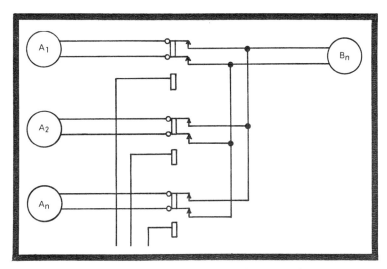

Fig. 2-9. Multiples in a connecting network

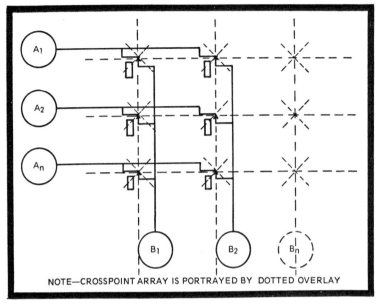

NOTE—CROSSPOINT ARRAY IS PORTRAYED BY DOTTED OVERLAY

Fig. 2-10. Multiples build up into a crosspoint array.

switch. The circuits that control the switching of the relays must insure that only one relay in any row or column is ever operated at any one time.

The Link Principle

Another arrangement, known as a **link**, provides a means for making one connection for many interconnections. Two multiples may be joined back-to-back through a common link so that any **A** circuit may reach it by means of a **multiple** on a set of relays and then reach any one of the **B** circuits by a similar **multiple** on a second set of relays. As shown in Fig. 2-11, two relays—one in each multiple—must be operated to establish a connection. Thus, the link principle provides a means for proportioning the amount of switching equipment according to the demand for simultaneous connections between two groups of terminal circuits. Set forth in a Swedish patent in 1912 by Betulander and Palmgren, the link principle permits the combination of primary and secondary switches much smaller in size than a single large selector. As shown in Fig. 2-12, the use of multiples and links may be represented by the symbols of Fig. 2-8B.

28

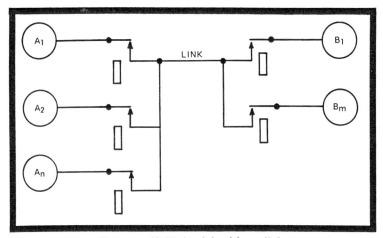

Fig. 2-11. Multiples joined by a link.

Availability and Grading. A link switch group is used most efficiently when all inputs have full access to all the links or trunks of the output group. Under this condition the system is said to have full availability. If some of the links or trunks are not accessible, the system is said to have limited availability. Frequently the size of a trunk or link group is too great to permit wiring of the group as a whole to each switch requiring access to that group. There are various ways in which this problem can be treated, one of which is through the use of the **graded** multiple. With this technique some fraction of the total

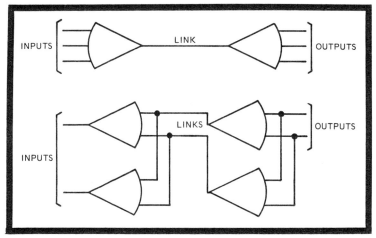

Fig. 2-12. Links connect primary and secondary switches.

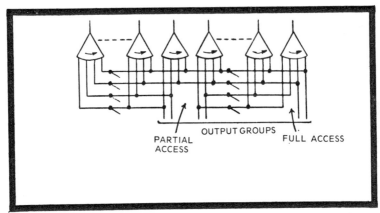

Fig. 2-13. Some outlets have only partial access in a graded multiple.

outputs are wired on a partial-access basis and the remainder are wired as a full-access multiple across all the switches. Such an arrangement is shown in Fig. 2-13. The use of graded multiples or grading is most effective in step-by-step exchanges, where the partial-access groups can be placed on the switches first in the order of hunting and these switches always start hunting at the beginning of the group. If this is not done, the advantages of the graded multiple are lost. Even then, calls from an input group will be left connected to the common output group after connections to the partial group have become idle, so it is evident that graded multiples can never be as efficient as full-access multiples.

Applying the Principles. The purpose of grading is to increase the volume of traffic carried by the lines. In applying it, the multiple of the switching stage is split up into as many subgroups as required to raise the number of outlets above that of the lines to be connected. Some are connected to a single subgroup, while others are connected to two or more subgroups. Where n is the number of subgroups, c_i the number of outlets available for the commons of order i, i is the ordinate of the common lines, N the total number of lines going out in the specified direction, and k the number of outlets available in the specified direction,

$$nk \geqq N$$
$$k = \Sigma c_i$$
$$N = \Sigma a \frac{1}{i} c_i$$

In the calculation of grading, the interconnection formula of $B = (A \diagup N)(K)$ gives the approximate grade of service, where A is the traffic offered in erlangs. For large values of A and N this formula gives a good approximation for pure chance traffic.

Homogenous grading is another technique in which the outlets are tested for the busy condition from the position occupied at the last busy test rather than starting from a home position. Only commons of a single order are used and the lines are connected on the principle of perfect combinations. Such a technique is applicable to rotary or crossbar switches.

SWITCHES, ARRAYS, AND GRIDS

In Fig. 2-10 we have already seen how a combination of multiples and links builds up to a crosspoint matrix. A coordinate representation of such a matrix is shown in Fig. 2-14. Crossbar switches, reed relays, or solid-state switches may be used to make up such a set of contacts. The particular type of switch selected for a given design would depend upon a number of factors, including economics as well as various performance characteristics. Because of the large number of such switch matrices in a single exchange of any size, a matrix is usually represented by a block diagram, as in Fig. 2-15A, with the numbers inside the block indicating the number of horizontals and verticals in the matrix. A single stage of switching is generally made up of several matrixes, the number being indicated by the number following the x sign

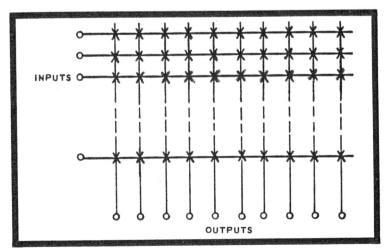

Fig. 2-14. Coordinate representation of a crosspoint matrix.

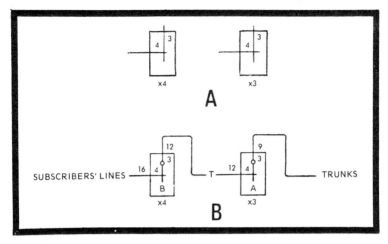

Fig. 2-15. Symbols for crosspoint arrays.

below the block. When two such stages are connected together, a 2-stage array is formed as shown in Fig. 2-15B. The **T** indicates that there are transpositions in the interconnections.

Another approach is to refer to a crosspoint array or matrix as a switch block and to call the combination of such blocks or stages a grid network, or simply a grid, as shown in Fig. 2-16. There are several variations in the symbology used in switching diagrams, and sometimes a block is simply labeled in regard to its contents or one or more crossed lines

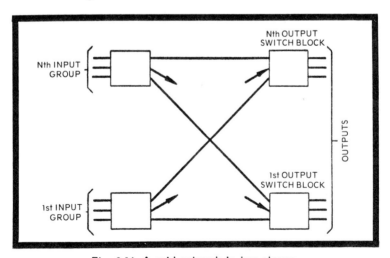

Fig. 2-16. A grid network in two stages.

are drawn to represent switching stages within the overall switching network. However, Figs. 2-15 and 2-16 will serve as a guide in examining the block diagram of the switching network of most exchanges employing space-division switching. Space-division switching is found in all circuit-switched exchanges other than those employing time-division switching, which will be covered later. All of the switching concepts that have been discussed in this chapter refer to the switching of circuits in space-division systems, where the speech or message paths are physically separated. However, the link principle is also utilized in time-division systems, where the speech or message paths are separated in time.

The number of matrix switches in a given stage of switching depends on the number of crosspoints in each array. Where the crosspoints and their associated components are expensive, as in the case of ferreeds or reed relays used in the switching networks of electronic exchanges, in general the matrix switches are smaller and more are required per stage. In the case of inexpensive crosspoints, the arrays consist of more contacts per matrix and fewer matrix switches are required per stage. Such is the case with crossbar switches, where more crosspoints per magnet are controlled. Other factors enter into the determination of the number of matrix switches in a stage, but these will be treated later.

Grid Networks .

Grid networks range from two stages of switching, in crossbar systems, to eight stages of switching, in some electronic systems. A general 2-stage grid network with its input switches designated as **primary** switches and its output switches designated as **secondary** switches is shown in Fig. 2-17. It is a basic requirement that each primary switch group have access via at least one link to each secondary switch group. It is important that the link spread between the switch groups be laid out in an orderly fashion for ease of control and administration. In the allocation of secondary terminations of links, the output terminal number on the primary switch designates the secondary switch number, and the primary switch number designates the secondary switch terminal.

To extend the 2-stage grid for connection to a particular output, it is only necessary to add a third stage, the links to which will duplicate the link spread between the first two

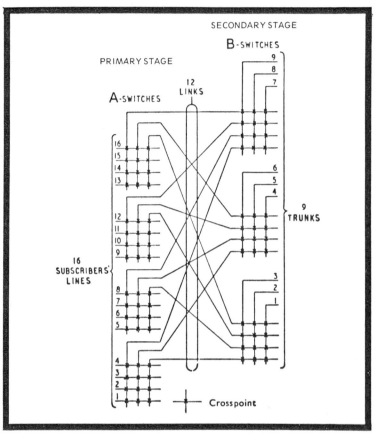

Fig. 2-17. 2-stage switching network.

stages. Such an arrangement is shown symbolically in Fig. 2-18. Assuming each stage consists of **n** switch blocks, any network input can be connected to any network output over **n** matching pairs of paths. To determine the set of **n** paths that can be used, you need to know only the input and output switch blocks involved. However, because of the relatively limited number of paths it provides, the 3-stage grid network is generally useful only for small exchanges.

In the larger electromechanical exchanges, the switching network is usually made up of two stages of primary-secondary grids, and is in effect a 4-stage grid. The fourth stage, which results from the splitting of the secondary switches to give an increased link spread within the network, is actually the primary stage of the output grids. Because of this it is not necessary to distribute the interconnections between grids (referred to as **junctors**) in the same way that links are spread out within a grid. It is only necessary that at least one junctor per secondary switch of each input grid connects to one primary switch of each output grid, which provides a minimum of one junctor to match any pair of originating and terminating links.

Traffic balance must be maintained carefully on the grid inputs and outputs, because the junctors from each input grid are divided equally among all output grids. If excessive traffic reached a particular output grid, the probability of failure to match due to busy junctors might be too great. Generally an attempt is made to obtain as wide a distribution as possible, over both switches and grids, to minimize the effect of switch or circuit troubles and to handle traffic with an optimum grade of service. With electromechanical systems, 4-stage networks have been adequate for the largest central offices. However, larger central offices with higher speed electronic common control has resulted in systems with up to 8-stage networks.

Concentration and Expansion Stages

As mentioned previously, switching systems may be considered as nondirectional from the viewpoint of being able to serve subscribers on either side of the system. However, in the progressive type of switching network (stepping, rotary, and panel) the path establishment of a call is inherently unidirectional; and the diagram of concentration, distribution, and expansion shown in Fig. 2-6 represents the interconnection functions. The grid type of network differs in

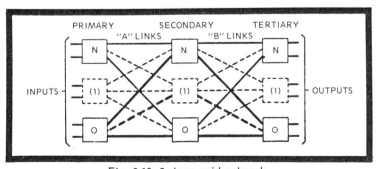

Fig. 2-18. 3-stage grid network.

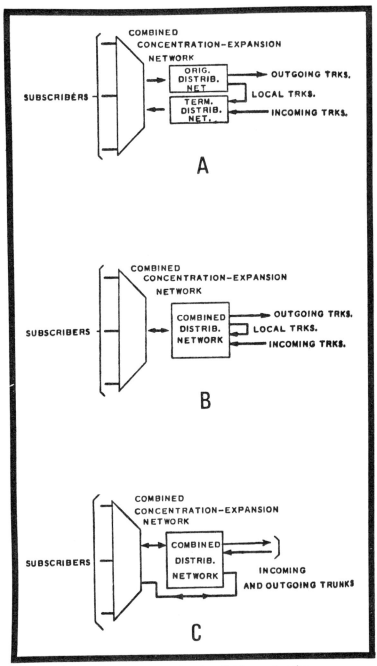

Fig. 2-19. Bidirectional switching networks.

that in the path establishment between two terminal points is bidirectional, and either point may be considered to be the input. By taking advantage of this feature it is possible to use parts of the grid network for both originating and terminating purposes. More efficient use of the switches and interconnecting links and junctors is realized, and the combination of the concentration and expansion stages offers the additional advantage of requiring only one appearance on the network for each subscriber line. In Figs. 2-19A, B, and C, three forms of combined networks are shown. In that of Fig. 2-19A, which is used in the No. 1 crossbar system, the originating and terminating distribution stages are separate for the most part, but the concentration and expansion stages are common. In that of Fig. 2-19B, which is used in the No. 5 crossbar system, all stages are bidirectional and inputs and outputs appear at both ends of the network. In that of Fig. 2-19C, which is used in an electronic system, only one connection is normally used through the distribution stage on each call. The connection may be established in either direction—that is, either side of the distribution network may be the originating

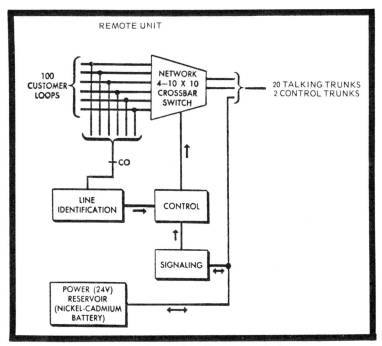

Fig. 2-20. A crossbar line concentrator.

side. This type of operation is possible because the supervision and battery supply are functions of the line circuits, in this case, so that there is no need for intraoffice trunk circuits.

Combined concentration-expansion switching networks utilize the links between the concentration-expansion stages and the distribution networks very efficiently when properly designed. This is in sharp contrast with the inefficient use of subscriber lines, which are used only 5 to 10 percent of the time even during the busy hour. One solution for this problem, which can be applied to both progressive and grid network systems, is the provision of line concentrators. Located remotely from the central office, such a concentrator is shown in block diagram in Fig. 2-20. Operating with its own control, it concentrates 100 subscriber loops to 20 talking trunks and 2 control trunks before they are fed to the central office.

Logic Switching Algebra and Control

3

Logic is considered to have started with Aristotle (384-322 BC), who laid down certain formal rules for use in reasoning, called the **laws of logic**. These include the rule of detachment and the rule of the syllogism. The former may be stated briefly as, "If P is true and if P implies Q, then Q is true." The latter may be stated briefly as, "If P implies Q and Q implies R, then P implies R." Many of the classical syllogisms take this form. Logic as set forth by Aristotle was the first attempt to present the general form of language and argument in a systematic fashion. Little change in this approach took place for more than 2000 years, and the subject of logic remained associated with the authority and prestige of Aristotle. However, the 17th century mathematician and philosopher, Liebniz, began to seek an algebra for reasoning to replace the use of statements. Much of this work was not published until long after others had duplicated his conclusions.

Around the middle of the 19th century, George Boole published a book on the mathematical analysis of logic, in which he presented logic as a form of nonquantitative algebra. His mathematics was an algebra of classes and of processes of selecting and conjoining classes. Boole expressed what he called the **laws of thought** in an algebraic form, which was illustrated by the English mathematician Venn in the late 19th century in a form that utilizes the concept of **sets** and **subsets**. The four forms of traditional logic can be shown as in Fig. 3-1 by Venn diagrams. Using the same method one can present the solution of a syllogism as shown in Fig. 3-2.

Besides applying to classes, Boolean algebra applies to propositions. For the statement, "If proposition A is true, then proposition B is true," the algebraic expression $A(1-B)=0$ may be written. For the **conditional proposition,** "If A is true, then B is true," $a(1-b)=0$; but A is true, that is $a=1$. Therefore, B is true; that is, $b=1$. For the **disjunctive** proposition; either A is true, that is, $a(1-b)$—or B is true, that is, $b(1-a)$. Then their

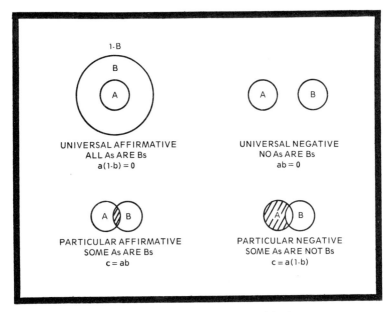

Fig. 3-1. Four forms of traditional logic.

sum is given by a—2ab + b=1. However, if A is true, a=1; so B is not true, b=0. By such mathematics Boole showed that his algebra deals first with classes, and second with propositions where the values are limited to true or false (1 or 0).

BOOLEAN ALGEBRA AND CIRCUIT SWITCHING

In 1938 Claude Shannon of the Bell Telephone Laboratories showed that Boolean algebra could be applied to the analysis of switching circuits. It is true that switching systems in various fields were developed prior to Mr. Shannon's work; and certainly step-by-step, rotary, panel, and crossbar systems evolved without the use of his theory. However, Boolean algebra has provided a more systematic approach to all types of switching problems, and all of the above systems can be analyzed by its methods. It has been particularly useful in the computer field. Since electronic switching in the telecommunications field is based on computer techniques, Boolean algebra is of equal importance there as well.

Boolean algebra, a mathematics dealing with **truth values**, provides the symbology for representing the truth or falsity of propositional statements and, as described above, is seen to deal with propositional logic. Since truth values may be represented by 1 and 0, so that true is represented by 1 and false is represented by 0, it is logical to associate them with closed and open switches. In the case of the closed switch, the value of 1 is established, while in the case of the open switch the value of 0 is established. However, here 1 and 0 are not used in any numerical sense, but as logical values. In the binary number system there are only two symbols, 1 and 0, so we see a compatibility between Boolean algebra, binary numbers, and digital systems in general.

In fact, in the design of digital systems, the usual procedure is to develop a set of logic equations describing the operation of the required system. These logic equations are written according to the rules of Boolean algebra, so a proper understanding of this algebra and the methods of simplifying its expressions is essential for the designer of logical switching systems. Simplification of logic equations is of great importance in most digital systems using large numbers of logic elements, since it is only in this way that the economical implementation of the switching system design can be realized. The development of most telephone switching systems now in use preceded the wide application of digital techniques in computer systems. However, the control portion of all telephone switching systems is digital, despite the fact that the message signals have been analog in their nature until the advent of data transmission by digital methods. Therefore, the same basic techniques are applicable to the control portion of communication switching systems as to digital computers and other digital systems.

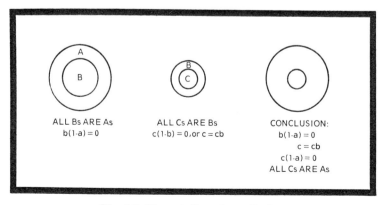

Fig. 3-2. The solution of a syllogism.

Logic functions are often deeply woven into the components of the switching system as in the case of Strowger step-by-step switches, where under direct control, the digital switching function is inseparable from the switching of the message circuits in the inherent design of the mechanism.

Shannon's work led to the term **switching algebra** as an application of Boolean algebra. In his treatment of the subject, Shannon changed his notation away from that of Boole, and used 1 for **false** or an open circuit, and 0 for **true** or a closed circuit. He did so because he dealt in terms of hindrance to current flow, so that 0 meant no hindrance and 1 meant the opposite. Also, he used the plus sign for AND and the multiplication sign for OR. Of course, using exactly opposite terms from those used by Boole created no change in the final analysis. After Shannon showed the way, however, modern notation reverted to Boole's notation in the application of Boolean algebra to switching problems.

The Basic Connectives of Boolean Algebra

Three basic connectives of Boolean algebra are =, + and ·, which are defined as follows for the variables A, B, and C:

(1) The connective = represents equivalence. Thus, A = B asserts that A and B have the same logical properties or the same truth value.

(2) The connective + means OR. Thus, if A **or** B represent the logical value 1, then A + B = 1.

(3) The connective · means AND in the sense that A and B equal 1 **only** if both A and B represent the logical value 1. That is, A · B=1 if A=1 and B=1. Just as in ordinary algebra, it is customary in Boolean algebra to omit the center dot and write AB instead A · B. Thus, AB also means A **and** B. In AB, the connective and its meaning are "understood."

In addition to the above connectives there is the operator indicating negation or complementation. It has the effect of reversing the truth value, as if A=1, $\overline{A}$=0.

Axioms and Postulates of Boolean Algebra

With the above connectives and operators it is possible to state certain laws in Boolean algebra as follows:
A + B=B + A (commutativity of the connective +)

$A \cdot B = B \cdot A$ or $AB = BA$ (commutativity of the connective)
$A + (BC) = (A + B)(A + C)$ (distributivity over the connective)
$A(B + C) = AB + AC$ (distributivity over the + connective)
$A + A = A$ (idempotent law)
$AB = \overline{A} + \overline{B}$
$A + 0 = A$
$A + \overline{A} = 1; \overline{A + A} = 0$
$A \cdot 1 = A$
$A\overline{A} = 0$
$(A + B) + C = A + (B + C)$ (distributive law)

Symbols for the Basic Connectives and Operators

While there are a number of systems used to represent the connectives and operators of Boolean algebra, there has been some standardization in the U.S., and the diagrams in Fig. 3-3 are typical for AND, OR, and NOT as applied to positive logic.

The logical action of the above block symbols can be illustrated by a **truth table** (Table 3-1) in which the logical value of any given function of the Boolean variables is tabulated in terms of all possible values of the variables involved. By definition, the logical value of a function can only be 0 or 1.

Table 3-1. **Truth Table for AND, OR, and NOT Functions.**

A	B	A B	A + B	$\overline{A}$
0	0	0	0	1
0	1	0	1	1
1	0	0	1	0
1	1	1	1	0

Basic Theorems

Boolean algebra is so related to set theory in mathematics that the AND, OR, and NOT functions may be represented by Venn diagrams as shown in Fig. 3-4.

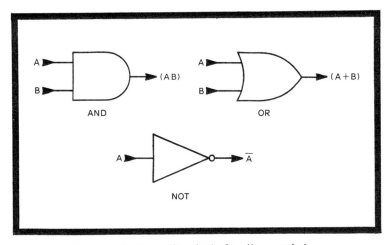

Fig. 3-3. Basic positive logic function symbols.

With the aid of Venn diagrams or truth tables, or by propositional algebra, the following theorems may be deduced. Their derivations are interesting mathematical exercises, but it is not necessary for us to derive them here.

Commutation
Association
Distribution
Union and Intersection
Indempotency
Absorption
De Morgan's Theorems

$A + B = B + A$ ... $AB = BA$
$A + (B+C) = (A + B) + C$ ... $A(BC) = (AB)C$
$A + (BC) = (A + B)(A + C)$ ... $A(B + C) = AB + AC$
$A + 0\ A;\ A \cdot 1\ A;\ A + 1 = 1;\ A \cdot 0 = 0$
$AA = A$ ... $A + A = A$
$A + AB = A$ ... $A(A + B) = A$
$\overline{A + B} = \overline{AB}$ ... $\overline{AB} = \overline{A} + \overline{B}$

LOGIC GATES

Out of 16 possible logic functions that can be realized from 2 Boolean variables; in addition to the AND, OR, and NOT functions; the following 6 are of significance in digital circuit designs: NAND, NOR, AND NOT (inhibit), OR NOT, coin-

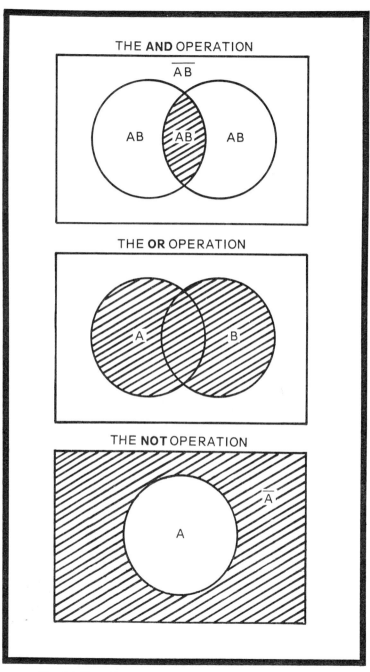

Fig. 3-4. Venn diagrams of AND, OR, and NOT operations.

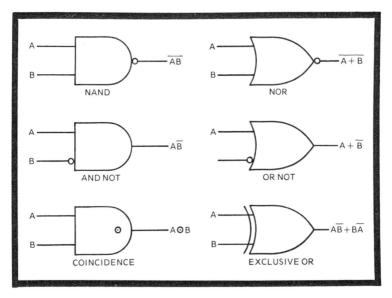

Fig. 3-5. Six additional important logic functions shown for positive-going outputs.

cidence, and exclusive OR. These functions are shown in Fig. 3-5.

The functions that we have just described are represented in hardware by **logic gates**, which control the propagation of signals through them and produce outputs in accordance with the logic function represented. The inputs and outputs of the gates are a set of 2-state signals or pulses. The American National Standards Institute has adopted the block symbols shown in Fig. 3-6 to represent gates for the nine types of logic functions mentioned above. Any of these gates, except the inhibit and OR NOT gates, may have any number of inputs but all of them have just one output.

Positive-Going and Negative-Going Logic

When signal levels are used to convey information, the logic is defined as direct-current or **dc logic**. When changes in signal level are used to convey information, the logic is defined as alternating-current or **ac logic**.

In the case of dc logic, if a higher voltage indicates the binary 1 state and a lower voltage indicates the binary 0 state, the logic is called positive-going or **positive logic**. If the higher voltage represents 0 and the lower voltage represents 1, the logic is called negative-going or **negative logic.**

Generally the choice of circuit components determines whether positive- or negative-going logic is used. Here we are mainly concerned with dc logic, and we will confine our coverage to the circuit elements required to produce the nine types of gates already mentioned.

Relay Logic

Since the inception of automatic telephone switching systems, relays have been used to implement logic functions. With closed or open contacts they can deliver a binary 1 or 0 output, respectively. The nine gates already mentioned can be produced by rather simple relay circuits—three of which are shown in Fig. 3-7. Relays are still being used extensively in electromechanical switching systems to implement logic functions, especially in common control circuitry. However, they are much slower and less reliable than the solid-state electronic gates that have replaced them to a considerable extent.

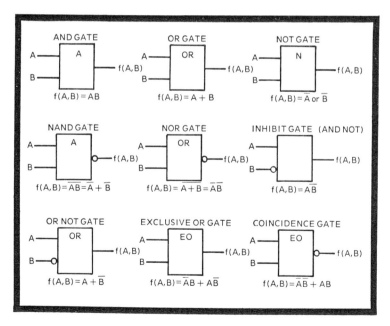

Fig. 3-6. American National Standards Institute symbols for 9 important logic gates.

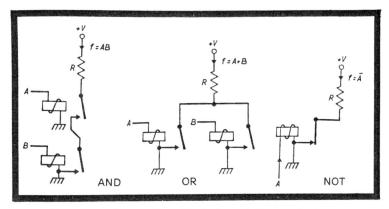

Fig. 3-7. Implementation of logic through the use of relays.

SEMICONDUCTOR LOGIC FAMILIES

Diodes and transistors are used in various combinations to implement the nine logic functions—AND, OR, NOT, NAND, NOR, OR NOT, exclusive OR, inhibit and coincidence. Semiconductor diodes operate as fast switches in AND as well as OR operations, as shown in Fig. 3-15. However, since they are passive devices, they are usually combined with transistors to provide more sophisticated gating action.

Diode–Transistor Logic (DTL)

Diode-transistor gates are widely used in both discrete and integrated form. A typical circuit is shown in Fig. 3-8. The number of inputs to the circuit is called the **fan-in.** The number of outputs is the **fanout.** The fanout is determined by the output-driving capability of the circuit, and represents the number of unit input loads that can be connected to the output. In this circuit, when the voltage on all of the inputs corresponds to that of the **high state,** the diodes are non-conducting and the transistor saturates, giving a **low-state** output. If any one input is taken to the low state, its diode conducts and the voltage across the two level-shifting diodes is insufficient to allow current to flow into the base of the transistor. The transistor turns off and the output changes to the high state.

If the high-state voltage level is chosen to represent a logical 1 signal, the truth table corresponds to that of the

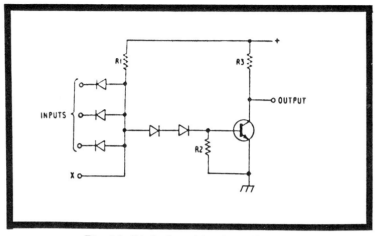

Fig. 3-8. Diode-transistor logic (DTL).

NAND operation. Conversely, if the low-voltage level is chosen to represent a logical 1 signal, the truth table corresponds to that of the NOR operation. Therefore, the circuit of Fig. 3-8 can be used as either a NAND or a NOR gate, depending upon whether positive or negative logic is utilized.

A modified version of diode-transistor logic is shown in Fig. 3-9, where one level-shifting diode is replaced by a transistor with its collector taken to a tap on the input resistor. This transistor cannot saturate, and the additional gain it introduces enables a higher base current to be used to drive the output transistor, without at the same time increasing the current drawn from an input in the low state.

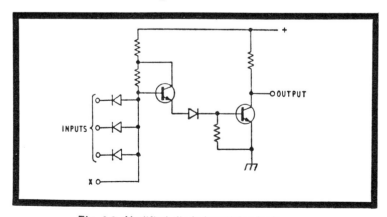

Fig. 3-9. Modified diode-transistor logic.

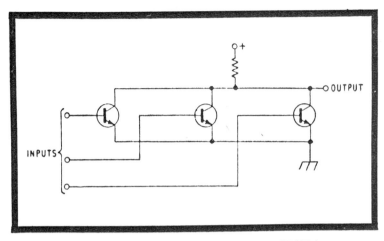

Fig. 3-10. Direct-coupled transistor logic (DCTL).

Direct-Coupled Transistor Logic (DCTL)

Transistors may be used directly without diodes in logic gate circuits, as shown in Fig. 3-10. In fact, such circuits were among the first to be considered for construction in integrated form because of their simplicity. If any one or more of the three inputs shown is in the high state, the corresponding transistor will be turned on and the output will be in the low state. It is only when all of the inputs are in the low state that the transistors will be turned off and the output will be in the high state. Thus, the circuit provides the operation of a NOR gate in positive logic.

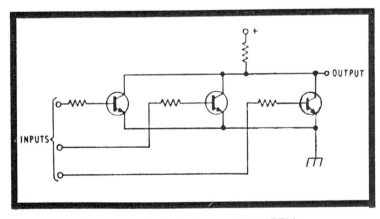

Fig. 3-11. Resistor-transistor logic (RTL).

Because of the so-called "current-hogging" characteristic of the circuit shown in Fig. 3-10, it is modified into what is known as resistor-transistor logic (RTL). Here, as shown in Fig. 3-11, resistors in series with each input limit the current and at the same time cause an increase in the high-state output level. A further modification may be provided by the addition of capacitors across each input resistor to give resistor-capacitor-transistor logic (RCTL). In general, a main disadvantage with direct-coupled transistor logic circuits is that the transistors are operated in saturation. This limits the ultimate speed of operation of the logic element.

Transistor-Transistor Logic (TTL or T²L)

TTL or T²L circuits are among the most advanced saturated-mode digital integrated circuits available. They are among the fastest in switching speed, lowest in power consumption, and highest in noise immunity of the high-speed circuits. In effect, the diodes of the diode-transistor logic are replaced by a multiemitter transistor, and the level-shift or coupling diodes between the input diodes and the first transistor are eliminated. The immediate benefit is that these diodes which could cut off too soon and cause blocking of the charge on the base of the output transistor and an excessively long turnoff time, are no longer in the circuit.

The basic TTL gate circuit, shown in Fig. 3-12, provides the same logical operation as the diode-transistor logic—a

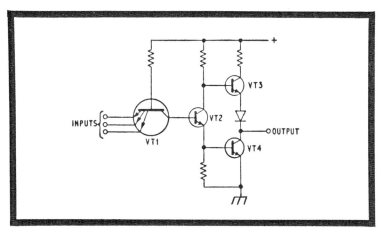

Fig. 3-12. Transistor-transistor logic (TTL or T²L).

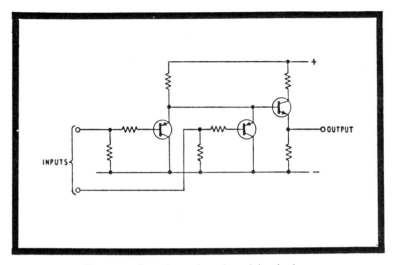

Fig. 3-13. Complementary transistor logic.

NAND function. When all the inputs are in the high state, current flows through the base resistor and the base-collector junction of transistor VT1 into the base of transistor VT2. Transistor VT2 saturates, turns transistor VT3 off and VT4 on, thereby giving a low output state. Transistor VT3 is called a **pullup** transistor and transistor VT4 is called a **pulldown** transistor. The diode in the output stage insures that transistor VT3 is turned off when transistor VT4 is turned on. When any one input is in the low state, the base current of transistor VT1 is diverted to its base-emitter junction and it saturates, providing a low-impedance path that enables VT2 to turn off quickly. Transistor VT4 turns off and VT3 turns on, giving a high-state output. The low resistance in the collector of the pullup transistor limits the current surge that can occur on switching.

Complementary and Current-Mode Logic (CML)

All of the transistor gate circuits considered thus far operate in the saturated condition. This type of operation limits their speed. Two higher speed nonsaturated types are complementary transistor logic and current-mode logic. As shown in Fig. 3-13, the basic complementary transistor logic gate is a noninverting AND. It is somewhat similar to modified diode-transistor logic in that pnp transistors are used in the inputs and several of these gates can be cascaded before the logic levels have to be restored. Either NOR gates or level-setting AND gates can be used for restoring the levels. Both have npn transistors on their inputs and delays of about 12 nanoseconds (nsec). The AND gate shown here has a delay of about 4 nsec.

In current-mode logic also the transistors do not saturate, and very fast operating speeds are attained because of the absence of delays caused by stored charge. A basic gate circuit of this type is shown in Fig. 3-14. With all outputs in the low state, emitter follower VT5 will be conducting to give a high-state output. Transistor VT4 will also be conducting, and the output from VT6 will be low. If any one input is taken to the high state, current will flow through the input transistor resulting in a low-state output from VT5. Because of the common emitter resistor, the current through VT4 will be reduced as that through the input transistor increases, resulting in a high-state output from transistor, VT6. Emitter followers are used at each output in order to restore logic levels. An advantage of this current-mode logic circuit is that complementary outputs can be obtained from the basic gate—a NOR output from VT5 and an OR output from VT6.

Current-mode logic gives delays of only a few nanoseconds, but it has a low noise immunity and a high power dissipation. Also, very high-speed circuits generally introduce problems with their interconnections, and there is no point in using them where their high speed is not essential.

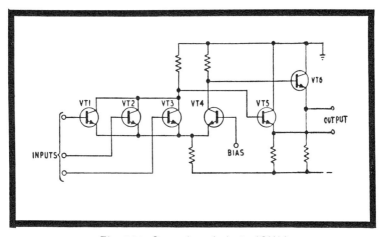

Fig. 3-14. Current-mode logic (CML).

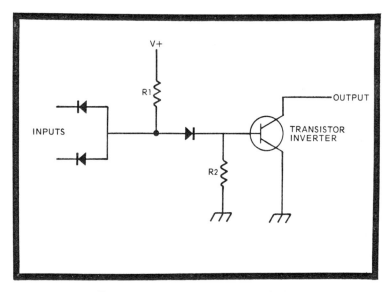

Fig. 3-15. AND NOT logic of No. 1 ESS.

SEMICONDUCTOR LOGIC IN ELECTRONIC COMMON CONTROL SYSTEMS

In the Bell System No. 1 ESS, the basic logic in the central control portion of the exchange is of the simplest type. A diode AND gate, followed by an inverting amplifier, provides an AND NOT building block, which is used throughout the control system. A biasing circuit is added to overcome the combined voltage drop of an input diode and the driving transistor's saturated voltage. This low-level logic circuit is shown in Fig.

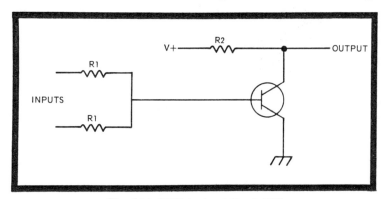

Fig. 3-16. NOR logic of No. 2 ESS.

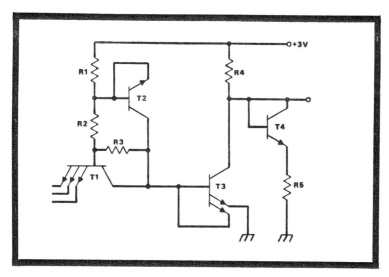

Fig. 3-17. NAND logic of Bell's 1A processor and No. 4 ESS (Diode-modified T2L or DT2L gate).

3-15. However, in most other electronic exchanges one will usually find one of the saturated-transistor types of logic.

In the No. 2 ESS the basic building block is a transistor-resistor NOR gate, as shown in Fig. 3-16. It is constructed of silicon transistors and tantalum-nitride thin-film resistors. In the Bell System No. 101 ESS PABX exchange two types of logic are employed. In the lower-speed portions of the common control, resistor-transistor logic using the Western Electric type 16C transistor is employed. A higher-speed logic is required in some portions of the control unit, for example, in the 1 MHz system clock and in translation portions of the storage systems. There, diode-transistor NOR gates are used.

In Bell's 1A processor, which is up to eight times faster than the No. 1 ESS processor, diode-modified transistor-transistor (DT^2L) NAND gates are used as the basic logic building blocks. These were developed to provide a fast, low-power gate with a 5 nsec propagation delay and a 6 mW power dissipation. The collector-diffusion isolation process used to produce these integrated gates has resulted in a worst-case noise margin of 200 mV. With a logic swing of one volt, this noise margin compares favorably with that of other types of gates. The circuit of the 1A processor's DT^2L gate is shown in Fig. 3-17.

 **4** # Circuit Switches and Relays for Speech and Control Circuits

A variety of metallic-path switches are used to open and close the speech-path circuits in modern communications switching systems. These range from rotary types, through the double-motion Strowger types, to various crossbar designs. Reed relays are also being more widely used in certain new electronic systems, where semiconductor or other solid-state switches have not proven to be satisfactory. Despite general use of metallic-path switches in the new electronic and computer-controlled exchanges, there are a few systems utilizing true electronic switching.

The more conventional relays, such as flat-spring and wire-spring types, are not used for speech-path switching, but are still used extensively in the common control sections of modern exchanges. The use of solid-state devices in such applications, however, has reduced the need for such electromechanical relays.

THE CROSSBAR SWITCH

The most widely used speech-path switch today is the crossbar type. Although it is distinctly an electromechanical device, it is being used in the switching network of a number of stored-program-controlled exchanges. The principle of operation of such a switch is shown in simplified form in Fig. 4-1. A series of horizontal- and vertical-wire multiples have contacts at each multiple intersection. By energizing the appropriate horizontal and vertical pair of magnets (from A to C and from W to Z, respectively), any vertical **inlet** can be connected to any horizontal **outlet.** Thus, energizing magnets A and W would connect inlet 4 to outlet 4. There are variations in the designs of the switch mechanisms in use—a main one having to do with whether the contacts are latched mechanically or electrically when in use.

The first crossbar offices in the U.S. were placed in operation in 1938. By 1943 a long-distance exchange was introduced and by 1947 the Bell System was fully committed to crossbar switching as it introduced its No. 5 crossbar system. Although the Strowger switch remained rather strongly in the picture, Bell replaced panel and step-by-step switching systems wherever possible with crossbar systems, until about 50 percent of their local lines were handled by such switches 25 years later. The independent telephone companies in the U.S. did not change appreciably from step-by-step switching during the same period, except for those served by the North Electric Company. By 1973 more than 850,000 independent lines were being served by crossbar switches, either imported from Swedish concerns or manufactured in this country under their license by North Electric. More recently, additional crossbar systems have been imported from Japan, where a large number of such switches have been made during the past decade.

Operation of a Basic Crossbar Switch

A crossbar switch manufactured by L.M. Ericsson, with 10 vertical and 6 horizontal select bars, is shown in Fig. 4-2. Despite its unique construction the crossbar switch belongs to the relay type of selectors, because its contacts are opened and closed by relay action. The vertical unit, shown in

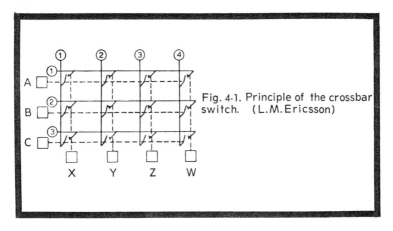

Fig. 4-1. Principle of the crossbar switch. (L.M. Ericsson)

Fig. 4-2. Typical crossbar switch made by L.M. Ericsson (L.M. Ericsson).

Fig. 4-3, consists of a magnet, D, an armature, E, and 12 springsets as determined by the number of horizontals—6 in this case. There are moving springs for every springset, but the fixed springs are in the form of a contact strip common to all springsets. When the springset is actuated, all moving springs are moved simultaneously by a lifting card.

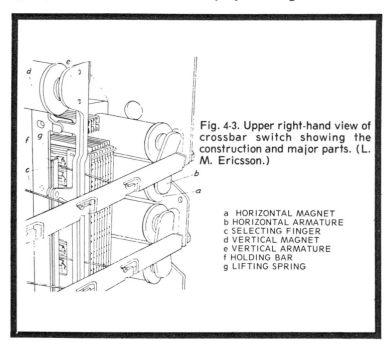

Fig. 4-3. Upper right-hand view of crossbar switch showing the construction and major parts. (L. M. Ericsson.)

a HORIZONTAL MAGNET
b HORIZONTAL ARMATURE
c SELECTING FINGER
d VERTICAL MAGNET
e VERTICAL ARMATURE
f HOLDING BAR
g LIFTING SPRING

The bars are mounted horizontally across the switch. Each bar armature can be attracted by one or the other of two magnets (A in Fig. 4-3) and the bar rotates in one or the other direction according to which of the two magnets operates. Note that a 6-bar switch has 12 horizontal magnets. Every springset in a vertical unit has one horizontal magnet which, however, is common to the corresponding springsets in all vertical units. When a horizontal magnet is energized, followed by a vertical magnet, the springset located at the junction of the horizontal and vertical rows is actuated and thereafter remains closed until the vertical magnet releases. The horizontal magnet is used only for the actual closing of the contacts, and releases as soon as the vertical magnet has operated.

A springset and selecting mechanism is shown Fig. 4-4. The method of arranging for the closing of a springset in a vertical unit is as follows: Every horizontal bar is equipped with a selecting finger, C, for every vertical unit. When horizontal magnet, H for example, operates, bar 1 rotates and the selecting fingers come into a position between the lifting card, L, of the first springset, with its associated lifting spring, G, and a holding bar, F. The vertical magnet, on operation, moves the holding bar in the direction of the lifting card and lifting spring. The shape of the lifting spring is such that the selecting finger is clamped by the holding bar at the same time as the lifting card is actuated, closing the contacts of the springset.

After the vertical magnet has operated, the horizontal magnet can release and the bar returns to its normal position.

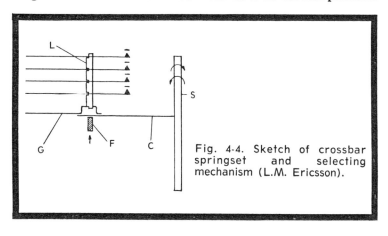

Fig. 4-4. Sketch of crossbar springset and selecting mechanism (L.M. Ericsson).

Owing to the resilience of the selecting finger, the bar can still move and may be used for the making of contacts in another vertical unit. If the selecting finger is not in position in front of the lifting card when the vertical magnet operates, holding bar F enters the U-shaped depression of lifting spring G, but cannot reach the lifting card to operate it.

Miniature Crossbar Switches

In recent years a main trend has been the development of crossbar switches somewhat smaller than the conventional types. These range from a Bell Labs unit requiring only 40 percent of the panel space of the conventional switch assembly and with 240 crosspoints, to a Japanese NTT unit only about one-eighth the size of a conventional switch with mechanical latching. Two other examples are ITT's Miniswitch and Northern Electric's Minibar switch. ~~Not. So .~~

When Northern Electric (~~Canadian affiliate of Bell Labs~~) embarked on the development of the Minibar switch, they decided that the new small switch had to meet the following requirements: (1) a significantly faster switching speed than the large crossbar switch, (2) a cost per crosspoint no greater than the large crossbar switch, (3) electrical compatibility with the standard crossbar switch, (4) increased switch capability to reduce the number of crossbar switch codes being manufactured, (5) provision of vertical units with a split multiple and adapted to operation of three crosspoints (two 3-wire and one 6-wire), and (6) improved performance and reliability.

The development activity of Northern Electric resulted in a 10 x 20 6-wire switch with 200 crosspoints of 6 make contacts each. The contacts are mounted in 20 vertical units, each containing ten 6-wire crosspoints. The stationary contacts are multipled in each vertical unit, and the moving contacts have terminals which are multipled by horizontal strapping. In operation, the Minibar switch is similar to the standard crossbar switch. Operation of a select magnet rotates the associated select bar and, by means of a select arm, a select finger located in the vertical unit is moved into its trapping position. Subsequent operation of a hold-magnet armature operates the crosspoint in which the finger is in the trapping position. Release of the select magnet restores the untrapped fingers to normal, but the finger of the operated crosspoint remains trapped until the hold magnet is released, after which the crosspoint and finger return to normal. A comparison of the MINIBAR with the 3-wire reed relay array and the 6-wire standard crossbar switch is given by Table 4-1.

Table 4-1. Comparison of Metallic-Path Switches

Per Cross-point Ratio	6-wire Minibar	3-wire Reed Array	6-wire Standard Crossbar
Cost	1.1 to 0.88	2.5	1.0
Volume	0.48 to 0.33	0.5	1.0
Weight	0.43 to 0.34	0.44	1.0
Operate Time	0.5	0.015	1.0

The **Miniswitch** of ITT is a miniature crossbar switch with a novel contact action. Each individual moving contact consists of a closely wound helix coil of precious-metal-coated wire. For the multiple, the contact is an open-wound helix at right angles to the moving contact helix. When they are brought together, the close helix nests into the open helix to give a twin contact. The matrix provides 256 crosspoints of 2 wires and 128 crosspoints of 4 wires. Although a direct comparison cannot be made in performance, due to the difference in wire capacity, the comparison of weight and size of the Miniswitch with a conventional 3-wire crossbar switch shows the high degree of miniaturization achieved. The conventional switch weighs 44.75 pounds and has a volume of about 1450 cubic inches, while the Miniswitch weighs 2.8 pounds and has a volume of about 80 cubic inches. An inside view of the Miniswitch is shown in Fig. 4-5.

The Crossbar Code Switch

Another approach to reducing the size and weight of the crossbar switch is that used by L.M. Ericsson in their **code** switch, which introduces binary code-bar selecting similar to that used in teleprinters. The multiples are placed in a row one after the other with code bars below the multiples, instead of in the conventional arrangement with vertical units and traversing horizontal selecting bars which obstruct observation and accessibility. In this design the vertical magnets receive only a short current impulse, when the selected multiple position is connected, and are consequently

Fig. 4-5. Inside view of ITT's miniswitch (ITT—International Telephone and Telegraph Corp.).

dead during a call. This results in a reduction in power consumption, which is of importance in some applications.

In the code switch, V contacts are introduced. The multiple is built up of single-wire springs provided with sleeves of contact material which, with twin action, make contact with V-shaped contact strips. The wire springs provide compact multiple banks with small dimensions but adequate observation facilities. They are efficiently self cleaning and are locked against the V contact in the connected position.

Compared with the conventional switch, the height of the code switch is one-half as much. Overall, the code switch has a volume less than one-third and a weight about one-third that of the conventional switch.

REED RELAYS

Reed relays have become popular as circuit switches in the speech paths of electronic exchanges, due to their high operating speed. They also have the advantages of low operating-power requirements and excellent crosstalk characteristics. The sealed dry-reed switch was developed by Bell Laboratories with telephone switching applications in mind and its first application was in the center conductor of a coaxial line. Reed-relay development at Bell Laboratories led in two basic directions—one in which the reed capsule was filled with hydrogen, helium, nitrogen, or other gases, depending upon the application, and the other in which the capsule was wetted internally with mercury. To distinguish the former type from the latter, it was called a **dry-reed relay**.

Figure 4-6 shows a dry-reed relay in its simplest form, while Fig. 4-7 shows the principle of action of a reed switch. One method of actuating a reed switch utilizes a current through a coil wound around the switch. Another way involves the introduction of a magnetic field in close proximity to the relay. In either case the principle of action is the same. The reed switch is magnetized in the axial direction by the effect of the coil or magnet so that the reeds attract each other. As the attraction overcomes the resilience of the reeds, the contacts close in a snap action.

Bell System Ferreed

The original standard-sized reed capsule has dimensions of 2.1 inches by 0.22 inches, while the miniature reed switch has capsule dimensions of 0.875 inch by 0.6 inch. An intermediate-sized unit, 1.25 inches by 0.17 inch, has been developed by Bell Laboratories for use in their ferreed design, shown in Fig. 4-8. Designed as a fast-acting switch with low

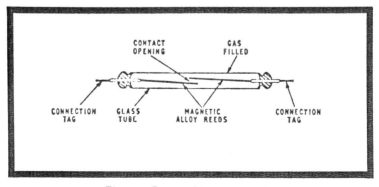

Fig. 4-6. Dry-reed-relay capsule.

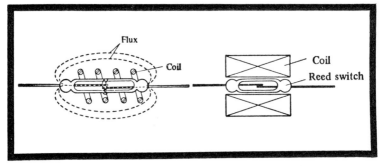

Fig. 4-7. Flux from A coil around A reed-relay capsule controls its operation.

power requirements for electronic switching systems, it consists of two sealed reed switches, which are operated and released by controlling the magnetization of two adjacent rectangular **remendur** plates. Remendur is a magnetic material—an alloy of iron, cobalt, and vanadium—with a square hysteresis loop. Each plate is magnetically divided into two independent halves by a low-carbon-steel shunt plate, which also provides the mechanical structure for assembling the crosspoints in various arrays of 8x8 switches. When the two halves of each plate are magnetized series-aiding, the flux from both plates returns through the sealed reeds, causing contact closure. When the two plate halves are magnetized in series-opposition, the return flux through the reeds' gap is reduced to practically zero and the contacts open. Current pulses in the coil set the magnetic conditions of the plates, so no power is absorbed except to change the open or closed condition of the contacts. The Bell System uses ferreed relays for speech-path switching in both their No. 1 and No. 2 ESS stored-program electronic switching systems. However, such close tolerances are required in the manufacture of ferreeds that no one outside of the Bell System has chosen to incorporate them in electronic switching systems.

Conventional Reed Relays

Wherever reed relays are used in other systems, a simple surrounding coil supplied by continuous current is employed. Reed relays in general are inherently fast-acting devices with operate times in the low-millisecond range. While ferreeds have operate times of 200 to 500 usec, the average open-type-

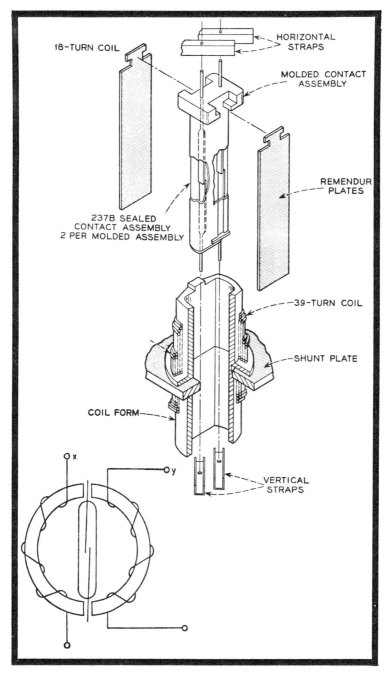

Fig. 4-8. Ferreed configurations (Bell Laboratories Record).

65

contact reed relay has operate times of 1 to 4 msec, and the average closed-contact reed relay has operate times less than 1 msec. Because of the slow operate times of other components in electronic switching systems, operate times of the average reed relay are adequate. Although miniature crossbar switches and reed relays offer little to choose between them in most respects for electronic switching systems, some feel that the faster switching speed, the greater bandwidth capability, and the better crosstalk characteristics of the reed relay will make it more desirable in future systems. However, the miniature crossbar switch does offer a component which can be standardized and widely used not only in stored-program electronic exchanges, but in wired-logic and electromechanical systems as well.

Reed relays are combined in groups of two or more per switching unit, depending upon the number of wires to be switched per call. In turn the individual switching units are assembled into crosspoint arrays, such as the 8x8 array of ferreeds mentioned above, to form a coordinate pattern.

SOLID-STATE ELECTRONIC CROSSPOINTS

In general, transistor crosspoints have been found to be poor in power handling and high in attenuation when in the on position, as well as high in cost. Therefore, there is very little application of such devices in the speech-path switching of present-day exchanges. One of the few examples of such application is found in the 2750 system of IBM. They experimented with transistors, including FETs, and came to the conclusion that silicon controlled rectifiers (thyristors) provided a practical crosspoint for application in their PABX designed to handle both speech and data signaling.

In line switching functions it was concluded that the crosspoint must have (1) two stable conditions—the on and off states, and (2) a high impedance in the off state with respect to the impedance in the on state. Since the impedance in the off state is generally capacitive, it determines the bandwidth of the system. A figure of merit for such a crosspoint is the ratio of the off impedance to the on resistance at audio frequencies. The crosspoint should possess a latch characteristic, so that once it is placed in the on state the crosspoint should remain on after the removal of the signal that turned it on. Other considerations are triggering-current requirements, holding-

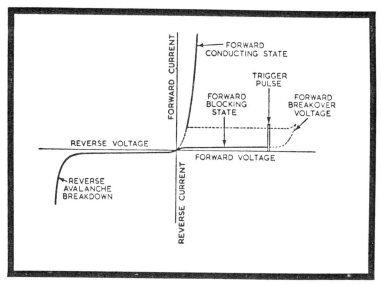

Fig. 4-9. Basic SCR operation.

current requirements, noise sensitivity, maximum voltage in the off state, and the **operate** (turnon) and **release** (turnoff) switching speeds. Also, the crosspoint must be adaptable to matrix arrays with selection circuitry that is isolated from the main signal path.

The individual crosspoint used for the switching network is composed of three parts integrated in the same silicon chip: a silicon controlled rectifier (SCR), a leakage resistor, and a selection diode. The SCR presents a nonlinear characteristic having two stable states. In the on state, it has a low dynamic impedance between its anode and cathode, with high current-carrying capability. In the off state, it has a high impedance for voice frequencies with a breakdown voltage of over 35V. The basic operational characteristics of an SCR are shown in Fig. 4-9. The three components mentioned above are integrated in the same silicon chip by a planar epitaxial technology, which presents a major advantage of increasing component reliability by minimizing the number of physical outlets. On a substrate, eight chips are assembled into four units of 1x2 array. The substrate is housed in a micro-module (0.5 inch by 0.5 inch) with 16 connection pins. A larger matrix is made by packaging up to 16 modules on a pluggable card (3 inches by 3 inches) which is the smallest replaceable unit in the switching network.

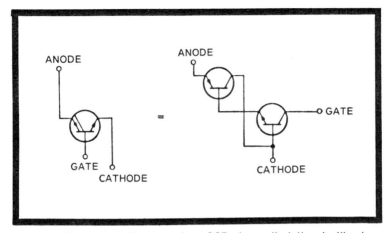

Fig. 4-10. Equivalent diagram of an SCR shows that it acts like two transistors.

A basic crosspoint of the above type is shown in Fig. 4-10, and matrix arrangement of such crosspoints is shown in Fig. 4-11. Switching speeds of this device are considerably higher than that necessary for line-switching applications. Typical operate and release times are in the range of 0.3 to 0.7 usec, and are typically governed by charge storage.

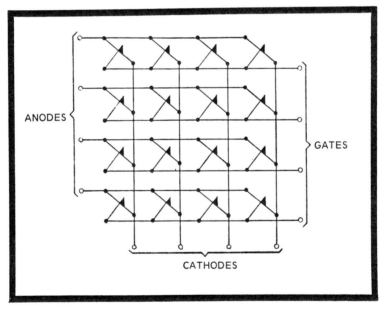

Fig. 4-11. Crosspoint of SCR switches.

RELAY-CONTROLLED AND MOTOR DRIVEN SELECTORS

Most of the world's telephones continue to be switched by either relay-controlled or motor-driven selectors. Although an engineer is not likely to be asked to design new versions of such switches, considerable quantities continue to be installed each year primarily for small exchanges of less than 2000-line capacities, and in cases where exchanges can be expanded most expeditiously by the addition of such switches. The principal relay-controlled switch is the Strowger type, which was conceived by Almon B. Strowger as early as 1889. Strowger switches are utilized in exchanges embodying the step-by-step principle. The principal motor-driven rotary

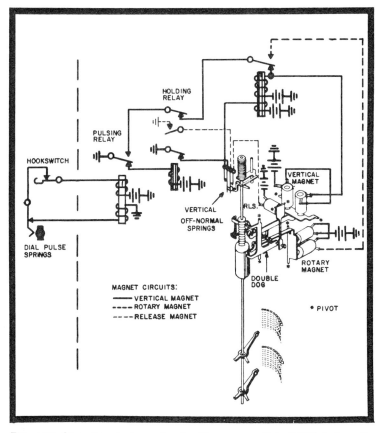

Fig. 4-12. Operational elements of a Strowger switch (GTE Automatic Electric Labs, Inc.).

selectors are the 7-series of ITT, the EMD motor-switch of Siemens and ITT, and the 500-line selector of L.M. Ericsson. Such motor-driven switches are used in **rotary** systems, which have been installed since the early 1920s.

Strowger Switch Operation

Shown in Fig. 4-12, the Strowger switch is the principal mechanism in step-by-step switching systems. It selects 1 out of a possible 100 circuits. A contact bank consists of 10 levels with 10 contacts per level. By first stepping vertically to the desired level and then rotating to the desired contact, any 1 of the 100 contacts is selected. Subscribers' dial pulses are used in conventional step-by-step systems to step selecting switches in central offices and thereby establish connections between calling and called telephones.

When the caller lifts his handset, the hookswitch closes the line circuit and operates the pulsing relay. The pulsing relay operates the holding relay, which in turn operates the sequence relay. Assume the caller wishes to step the switch wipers to bank-contact position 45. He dials 4. The dial opens the line circuit four times in quick succession. The pulsing relay, a quick-response relay, responds to the dial pulses. For each pulse, the dial opens the line circuit for about a sixteenth of a second, releasing the pulsing relay. Although the released pulsing relay opens the circuit of the holding relay, this relay has a copper sleeve to delay its release about a third of a second. Thus, the holding relay stays operated until the dial pulse springs reclose and the pulsing relay reoperates. Each time the pulsing relay restores, it sends a pulse of current through one of the sequence-relay windings and the vertical magnet in parallel. The first vertical-magnet pulse raises the switch shaft so that the vertical off-normal springs open the circuit of the second sequence-relay winding. However, the pulsing relay pulses through the first sequence-relay winding and the induced currents in the sequence-relay sleeve keep the sequence relay operated throughout the string of dial pulses— four in this example. The four pulses into the vertical magnet cause it to raise the switch shaft and contact wipers opposite the fourth bank-contact level. After the last pulse, the dial pulse springs remain closed, the pulsing-relay springs remain closed, the pulsing relay remains operated, and, after about a tenth of a second, the sequence relay restores.

In this example of Strowger switch operation, the caller wishes to connect to the bank contacts of line 45. Now, with the sequence relay released, when the caller dials 5, his dial opens the line circuit five times, and the pulsing relay restores five times and sends five pulses of current into the rotary-stepping magnet. This turns the shaft and wipers to line 45.

When the call has been concluded and the connection is no longer required, the caller hangs up. This time, instead of being briefly opened by dial pulses, the line circuit is opened

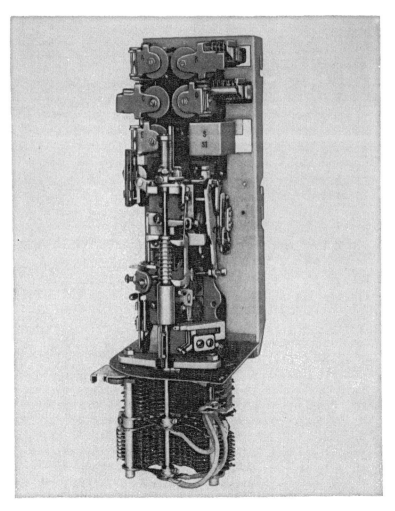

Fig. 4-13. Strowger selector used in step-by-step systems (Automatic Electric, Inc.).

for a longer time by the hookswitch. The pulsing relay restores immediately, and opens the circuit of the holding relay. The holding-relay sleeve keeps it operated for another third of a second; then the holding relay restores. As the pulsing relay responds to the dial pulses, the holding relay responds to the caller's hookswitch. In other words, the holding relay distinguishes brief breaks (i.e., dial pulses) from prolonged open circuits (i.e., hookswitch signals). The released holding relay closes the release-magnet circuit. The release-magnet armature withdraws the double dog teeth that have held the shaft and wipers in place. The helical spring on top of the shaft turns the shaft and the wipers back to the left, and off the bank contacts. Then gravity pulls the shaft down to its normal position. A shaft extension operates the **off-normal** contacts, which open the release-magnet circuit.

Figure 4-13 shows a typical Strowger selector switch manufactured by Automatic Electric, Inc., a subsidiary of General Telephone and Electronics Corp.

The 7-Series Rotary Switch

In the switch used in the ITT 7-series rotary system, the wipers or brushes are mounted in a die-cast frame called a brush carriage, which rotates in a clockwise direction and carries the brushes over the bank terminals. The 10 sets of brushes are positioned so that normally they do not make contact with the bank terminals during rotation of the brush carriage. Any one set of brushes can be tripped and unlatched so that during the rotation of the brush carriage this set will make contact with the bank terminals. The rotary level-selecting mechanism is called a **trip spindle**. It has 10 sets of fingers, and when positioned under the control of the sender, will cause a set of brushes, corresponding with the level or group of lines in which the calling subscriber number is found, to be unlatched. The trip spindle and the brush carriage are driven by flexible gears and the driving power is derived from an electric motor, which drives a vertical shaft on which the driving gears are mounted. An outline of a final selector of the 7A rotary system is shown in Fig. 4-14. Selectors of the first, second, third, and fourth groups are identical to the final selector except they do not have the commutator INT1.

The selector is provided with two control magnets, one that controls the meshing and unmeshing of the trip-spindle driving gears and one that performs the same function on the brush-carriage driving gears. The trip spindle rotates in a clockwise direction with each 30 degrees of movement being called a **step**. The speed of rotation is 14 steps per second, with each step bringing into operation a level-trip finger. A commutator, INT2, mounted on the trip spindle, creates revertive pulses which are received and counted by the sender to control the number of steps the trip spindle must make to determine the particular group of circuits. When the trip spindle has completed its movement and a set of brushes is unlatched at the required level, the brush carriage is rotated. The rotation of the brush carriage is to find an idle circuit in the particular group. These are the functions of group selectors. The final selectors select the tens and units and connect through to the called number.

The EMD Motorswitch

Recognizing that precious-metal contacts should be provided for the speech path in rotary switching systems, the Siemens Company of West Germany introduced in 1955 its

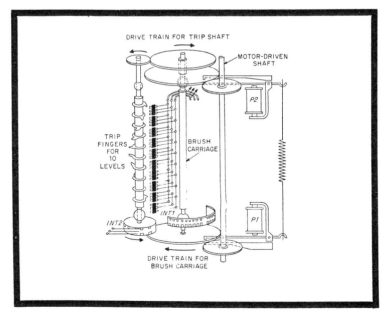

Fig. 4-14. Sketch of 7A rotary final selector (ITT—International Telephone and Telegraph Corp.).

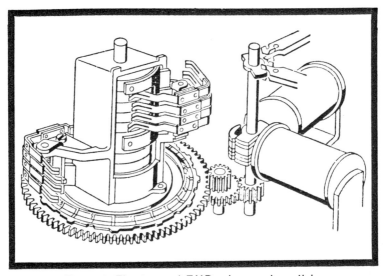

Fig. 4-15. The 4-armed EMD rotary motorswitch.

EMD motorswitch. EMD is an abbreviation of Edelmetall-Motor-Drehwahler, which translates into noble-metal uniselector motorswitch. This device has the qualities of having no rubbing contact with the speech-path contacts during rotation, being able to stop without vibration, and being able to operate at very high speeds for a mechanically rotated device. It accomplishes the first of these features by being arranged so that only after it has stopped on a required contact does a press-on magnet in the switch column press the switch arms of the speech wires against the mating bank contacts. An outline of an EMD motorswitch is shown in Fig. 4-15 with the two magnets which enable it to stop without vibration as well as control its rotation. If the two magnet coils are energized alternately at appropriate intervals, the Z-shaped armature assumes a continuous impact-free rotary motion. If both magnets are energized simultaneously, the switch mechanism stops without mechanical locking and vibration. The EMD motorswitch has a total of 112 outlets and rotates at such a high speed that it traverses 140 to 160 outlets per second. This means that it traverses a decade of switch contacts within the duration of a dial pulse or within about 100 msec.

Usually, EMD motorswitches employ silver-palladium contacts in the voice circuits and silver in control circuits.

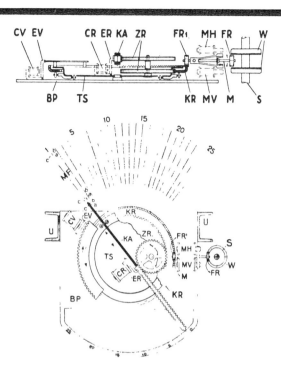

Fig. 4-16. L.M. Ericsson's 500-line selector (L.M. Ericsson).

a	a-contact of wiper arm and a-wire of multiple frame
b	b-contact of wiper arm and b-wire of multiple frame
B	pivoted guide for wiper cord
BP	base plate
c	c-contact of wiper arm and c-wire of multiple frame
CR	centering magnet for radial movement
CV	centering magnet for rotary movement
ER	detent controlling radial movement
EV	detent controlling rotary movement
FR	cog-wheels on shaft M
KA	wiper arm
KR	toothed ring (with teeth on both inner and outer edges)
M	spindle-carrying gear wheels FR and FR1
MF	multiple field (only one frame is shown fitted)
MH	magnetic clutch
MV	magnetic clutch
S	vertical shaft (driven by rack motor)
SP	supports for selector cord
TS	selector disc
U	selector rack
W	crown-wheel
ZR	cog-wheel for radial movement

Fig. 4-16B. Designation of components in Ericsson 500-line selector (L. M. Ericsson).

These metals do not develop objectionable oxidizing films, and contact resistance is held to a minimum. In addition, they exhibit elasticity combined with strength under compression—which is necessary due to the maximum pressure of 40 kg /cm^2 exerted on the speech-path contacts. In the EMD motorswitch, the wipers differ somewhat from the knife-edge type found in the conventional stepping and motor-driven uniselectors. Because of this they are called **contact arms** rather than wipers. Their rounded shape helps greatly to reduce wear on both the bank contacts and the contact-arm tips. Switches with four contact arms (as shown in Fig. 4-15) are used in the local telephone networks and switches with eight contact arms are used in the long-distance networks.

L. M. Ericsson's 500-Line Selector

L.M. Ericsson's 500-line selector is another rotary switching device. As indicated in Fig. 4-16, the selector mechanism can rotate around an axis and also move radially outwards. There are 25 possible angular positions, each of which places wipers opposite a row or **level** of bank contacts. Subsequent radial movements outwards from the center cause the wipers to pass over a level comprising 20 sets of bank contacts. The bank contacts, which also form the bank multiple, are constructed from radial rows of vertical bare wires with each level comprising 20 sets of negative, positive, and private wires. Since all motion is in a horizontal plane, the selectors are relatively flat and wide, allowing them to be mounted close together in vertical stacks. Figure 4-16 shows both top and side views of the 500-line selector.

The power shafting runs vertically up each stack of selectors and is parallel to their axes. The drive is from a pair of small, toothed, bevel wheels on the shaft, via a short spindle with toothed wheels at each end, to a pair of large bevel wheels on the selector. The small spindle is normally idling but can be tilted by electromagnets to either of two positions to impart forward or reverse rotary motion to the selector wipers. During the rotary level-selecting action, the wiper carriage is unlatched by a magnet and carried around with the large wheel until the wiper arm is positioned opposite the desired level. The magnet then releases to latch the carriage in that position. The wiper arm is next unlatched by another magnet and, because the wiper carriage is now locked in position, the drive is conveyed via the large wheel and the teeth on its inner rim to a pinion which drives a rack at the rear of the wiper arm. The rack in turn drives the wiper into and along the level.

Because the selector has 25 levels, they are not arranged in decimal order. The decimal number dialed by the subscriber must be translated in a register to a form which identifies the levels to be used. However, the register does not pass this information forward, but receives revertive pulses from the selector to determine when it should send forward a stop signal to arrest the rotary drive. This action is taken when the number of revertive pulses received in the register corresponds to the level to be used. Both the rotary disc and the wiper arm are equipped with cams to operate springsets during each step or stage of the power drive to take off the information required by the register. The system utilizing this 500-line selector was designed for local-exchange operation in large and medium-sized towns and cities but is said to have proved well adapted to smaller exchange areas, where multiples of 500 subscriber lines are accommodated. In large exchanges it has permitted a considerable reduction in the total number of selectors required. For multiexchange areas, local calls may be routed via one group;selector stage to 500-line final selector units, while junction calls are routed via an additional group-selector stage. In a very large installation of 60,000 lines, 20 levels of the first selector group would serve 10,000 local lines with levels from 21 to 25 available for serving 5 similar 10,000-line units. No call would be required to pass through more than two selector stages.

5 | *Control and Signal Methods*

Consideration of control and signaling methods require that the signaling portion of the communications system be viewed separately from the remainder of the system. However, signaling information shares the transmission media with whatever else may be presented to the switching system. For a long time it was common practice to refer to the remainder of the input as the speech or talking input; but today computer data, video, facsimile, and Telex are becoming increasingly important as inputs to switching systems. Therefore a more universal term, such as **message**, is more acceptable as descriptive of the remainder of the input to the system. So, as seen in Fig. 5-1, one may look upon the system as being fed by two separate sources: (1) a signal transducer, s, and (2) a message transducer, m. Each of these may comprise a number of devices for transducing in both directions—they may receive **and** transmit information. Hence, they can be designated as **rt units**, and both message and signal information are fed along a subscriber line to the first switch point, marked by a cross at the right. The solid arrowhead pointing at the switch indicates selective control.

Communications-switching control systems vary from complex to extremely complex when examined in detail, but an attempt is made here to illustrate functionally the various types of control systems without undue complication. The primary method we shall use is one orignated by T. H. Flowers of the British Post Office. Accordingly, various main items or portions of exchanges may be classified as receiving (r); receiving and transmittings (rt); and receiving, processing, and transmitting (rpt). In addition there are such items as random (ra) switches, access-send (a-s) switches, access-receive (ar) switches, and order wires (ow). Unfortunately, if one used only these designations some units could not be identified specifically by their more common names—registers, markers, and central processors, for example—so both designations will be used where the need for clarification demands it.

PROCESSING

The terms **processing** and **data processing** have been widely used in the computer field. The terms **processing** and **central processor** are similarly used in conjunction with electronic exchanges which employ computer techniques in their control functions. When one considers the fact that the term **processing** was not used in describing the operation of nonelectronic exchanges, it might be assumed that such exchanges do not have processing functions involved in their control. However, in any communications switching system, the orders for its control are derived from instructions in the form of signals received over local lines from subscribers and from instructions provided by the telephone operating company and stored in the exchange. The derivation of such controlling orders from signals and stored information is processing regardless of the type of switching system. Such a derivation of orders involves logical operations performed by logic switches. Any unit of an exchange which includes logic switches is called a processor. When viewed in this light it is seen that all communications switching systems, whether

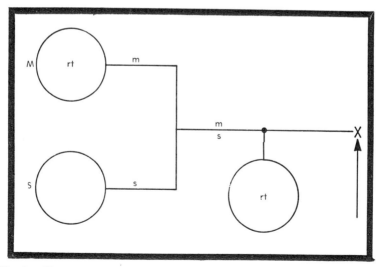

Fig. 5-1. Message and signal transducers in telecommunications systems.

they are electromechanically or electronically controlled, contain processing functions at one or more points in their circuitry. It is easier to understand the operation of all types of exchanges if processing functions are recognized in conventional systems as well as electronic systems. In effect, it is seen that all types of exchanges which work with rotary telephone dials incorporate digital processors, especially since the signaling currents generated by such dials are digital in character.

The ways in which processing functions are incorporated in electromechanical exchanges and electronic exchanges differ widely and, of course, the circuit elements that enter into the processing operations are very different. However, the basic objectives are the same in that orders are generated to make and break connections of the switches that intercept message paths or to control the switching network.

TYPES OF CONTROL

The control systems used in communications exchanges may be classified into three major types and some subtypes as follows:

(1) Direct control (also referred to as direct progressive control)

(2) Common control

    (a) Register progressive control

    (b) Register marker control

(3) Common stored-program control

The control method is related to some extent to the type of switching network employed. **Direct control** is associated with only progressive switching systems and primarily with step-by-step (Strowger) systems, although it can be applied to some rotary systems. **Register progressive** control has been applied to step-by-step systems through the use of directors and register-senders, and is generally used with rotary switching systems and the panel switching system—both of which have always depended upon registers to store the dialed digital-signaling information before it is processed and applied to control the switches in the network. With some rotary systems, marking operations are also added to register progressive control. However, the use of registers and markers has found its principal applications in the control of crossbar switching systems and electronic switching systems, which employ wired logic control. **Common stored-program** control is found only in electronic switching systems. However, in such systems the switching network may utilize reed relays, crossbar switches in various forms, or solid-state crosspoints. Also, either space-division or time-division switching may be employed with common stored-program control, which is sometimes referred to as **computerized switching.**

Control systems may utilize rotary switches, relays, crossbar switches, or a variety of solid-state electronic switching components, depending upon the type of control. The processors of all common-control systems depend upon the utilization of some form of memory. Memory units range from electromechanical relays in nonelectronic systems to sophisticated computer-type memories in common stored-program control systems.

Direct Control

Using Flowers' notation, a direct-control exchange may be shown as in Fig. 5-2. Although the receive-process-transmit units are shown separately, they are actually incorporated in the switching mechanisms themselves. In the step-by-step case, the selecting mechanisms of the Strowger switches react directly to the signaling impulses from the subscriber's dial. All but the last two digits of the called directory number, as signaled from the calling subscriber's instrument, operate the selector switches of the step-by-step system directly. The last

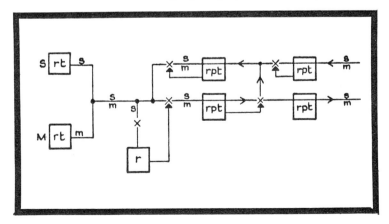

Fig. 5-2. Basic operations in direct-control system. (IEE—Conference Publications No. 52.)

two signaled digits control the operation of the connector (final selector) switch.

Actually, in step-by-step direct-control systems there are two variants from the simplified description just given. As will be discussed in more detail later, the subscriber may be connected to the selecting switches by either a line switch or a line-finder switch. Both of these are controlled indirectly.

In a typical arrangement for the line-switch method, the circuits of the attending function receive the calling signals from a subcarrier and notify an individual control circuit associated with the line switch. This control circuit drives the line switch to the first idle link and usually causes the removal of the **attention** signal. In the case of the line-finder method, there is no specific switch for a particular line to direct, so a type of common control is utilized. The attending functions of all lines associated with the same group of line-finder switches are tied together so that any one can actuate a control circuit that will select an available switch and (directly or via an individual switch control) cause the switch to find the calling line marked by the attending function.

These operations with line switches and line-finder switches have no bearing on the fundamental principles of direct control, but they show that in a practical, operating, step-by-step system there is an element of common control which can not be disregarded. Figure 5-3 shows block diagrams of the line-switch and line-finder control arrangements.

Sometimes direct control is referred to as **distributed** control. The basis for this description is obvious when one observes the fact that the control of the selecting switches is distributed throughout the system. It can be seen that such a distributed control is inefficiently used in that it is held all the time that a connection is in existence, despite the fact that it is in operation for only a second or two at the beginning of each call. Another disadvantage of direct control is that it dictates the use of small access switches, since large access switches are not readily controlled directly. Such a problem is overcome if provision is made for circuits which can accept signaling from the subscriber, translate it into another form, and reissue appropriate control signals to the switching network to guide the switches of a more efficient interconnecting network. Such circuits include a register called a **director, sender,** or **control register.**

Common Control

Common-control systems require the use of markers to store dialed digital information and may be used in conjunction with translators or with translators and markers. Historically, four basic variations of common-control

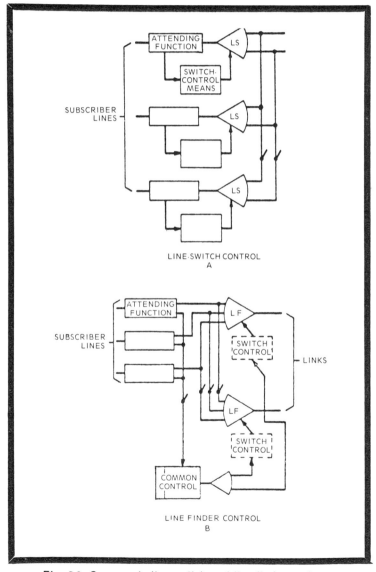

Fig. 5-3. Common in-line switch and line-finder systems.

technique have been employed with various types of speech-path switches, as follows:

(1) Digit storage in registers on a decimal basis and control of switches by stored digits without translation

(2) Digit storage in registers on a decimal basis with fixed translation and control of switches in a fixed pattern by such translated information

(3) Digit storage in registers on a decimal basis with readily alterable translation for any item of traffic, and control of switches by such translated information

(4) A variation of (2) or (3) in which markers are introduced to perform the function of hunting for idle paths in the switching network and completing the connection.

Methods (1) and (2) were used in early systems and (3) and (4) are used in modern systems. Most power-driven rotary and crossbar electromechanical switching systems use the basic method of (4), but with considerable variations. Electronic switching systems with wired logic use method (4) in a somewhat similar manner to that used by electromechanical crossbar systems, but with solid-state components and **some** relays instead of all relays.

Register Progressive Control. A control register may be applied to a progressive system by locating it ahead of the first selecting stage. As discussed under **Direct Control** the line finder in a progressive system operates independently of direct control by the dialed signals of the subscriber. Therefore, the control register may be inserted in the link between the line finder and the first selector stage as shown in the block diagram of Fig. 5-4A. However, since it will be operating for only a fraction of the holding time for each call, it is not necessary to provide a control register for each link. Hence, it is more practical to use the arrangment of Fig. 5-4B by providing a smaller number of control registers with separate access from several links ahead of the first selection stage. The number of control registers can be proportional to the links to provide the grade of service required.

After receiving the signaling information from the calling subscriber, the control register converts the received code into a form suitable for use by the control signaling circuits in a function referred to as **translation.** The register receives the signaling in the form of the directory number of the called subscriber, which identifies the trunk group to the desired central office and the called line in the central office. In general, two separate translations of the line number and the office code are required. The translating function, which will be described in greater detail later, may be an integral part of the control register or may be a separate unit. Generally, in modern systems it is a separate unit, because the translation process occupies but a short period of the overall holding time of the control register. Thus, separate translators may be shared by the control registers having access to them. For this reason, we find register-translators rather than just control registers in modern progressive switching systems.

Register control of progressive switching systems provides greater flexibility for switching through tandem offices and for alternate routing of calls. It is also possible to use switches with greater speed and access than in direct-control systems. The service requirements of metropolitan multioffice areas demand the trunking flexibility of register-translator control in progressive switching systems. Unfortunately, progressive switching systems are limited in that full use of alternate routing and second trial attempts are not

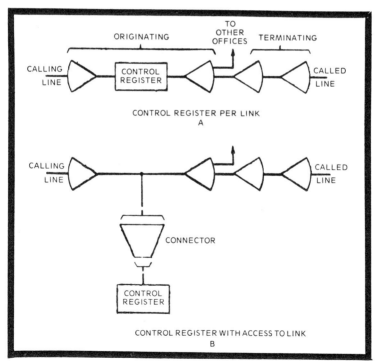

Fig. 5-4. The control register as applied to register progressive control.

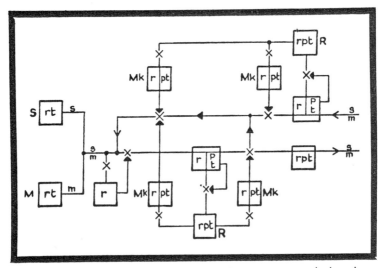

Fig. 5-5. Basic operation in a register-marker common-control system. (IEE—Conference Publications No. 52.)

possible because of the time factor. Economics often dictates against the full utilization of register-translator techniques with resulting limitations in the range and speed of interoffice signaling.

Register-Marker Common Control Although common-control principles are used in register progressive control systems, the selection of idle trunks in such switching systems requires the actual hunting by a switch. In the early 1920s thought was given to the selection or **marking** of a trunk by other means. Probably, the marker was developed originally to control switching networks with link systems. The various switching stages in a link system are interdependent, making it necessary to have a common unit which can supervise the state of the switching network and then select a switching path. Crossbar switches entered the picture during the 1930s in the U.S. It was necessary to group them into link systems, where marker control could be applied very effectively, in order to produce competitive exchanges.

In the basic register-marker common-control system of Fig. 5-5, subscriber lines have access to signal receiving-processing-transmitting units which are held only briefly during the setting up of each call. These units are common processors of registers, R, and markers, M. Equipment of this kind initially receives the dialed digits and subsequently sets up the connection through the exchange. Similarly, junctions at the incoming ends connect to common receiver-processor-transmitter (rpt) equipments which receive called-number signals and control the exchange switches. A more conventional block diagram showing register, marker, and translator with access to an interconnecting switching network is given in Fig. 5-6. The arrangement of these functions in electromechanical crossbar systems will be covered in more detail in Chapter 7.

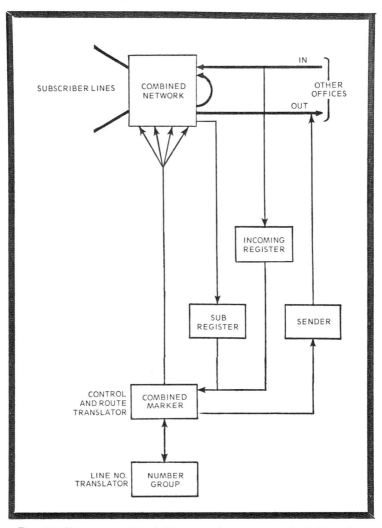

Fig. 5-6. More conventional diagram of common-control elements.

Translation

In a broad sense the translator in a telephone exchange might be like a language translator if one limits the language to the signaling information from the subscriber's telephone dial. The switching-control code in modern exchanges differs from the numerical code of the dialed directory number. The switches obtain access to the called subscribers by connecting to terminals for line equipment numbers or simply **equipment numbers**. In abbreviated form, one refers to the directory number as DN and the equipment number as EN. The line equipments correspond to subscribers' lines and are associated with subscribers' numbers on a purely arbitrary basis. The equipment numbers (EN) are not 4-digit numbers but each is in a series of five 1- or 2-digit numbers (a mixed number base) which indicate the locations of the equipments on the frames of the speech-path switching network.

Translation is used to convert the dialed decimal directory number to the nondecimal number forming the switching instructions, which the common equipment must have in order to reach a called subscriber. Such a conversion is referred to as DN-to-EN translation. Since the association of input and output codes is entirely arbitrary and must be changed from time to time to allow for changes in number assignments, it is apparent that a readily alterable arrangement is required. It is possible to use various combinations of relays to provide code translations, and some very elaborate translators have been and are being used with electromechanical crossbar systems. Since they usually accommodate at least 1000 numbers, a diagram will not be shown. In some designs 1000 coding relays are required, but by using a relay tree and separate cross connections it is possible to use resistors for output coding elements and thus reduce the complexity.

One translator which lends itself to better illustration is the ring type shown in Fig. 5-7. It has been used in the No. 5 crossbar system and is used in the electronic exchange that is about to be described in greater detail later in this chapter. Here a relay selection tree, under control of the input code, causes the connection of a 1-wire circuit to 1 of 1000 equipment-number terminals, each of which has a cross-connection wire that serves directly as the coding element for translating the associated equipment number. Each wire is threaded through a common array of ring-type cores with one core for each digit in each place of the output numbering scheme. After each equipment number selection has been made, a surge of current is passed through each wire. Acting as a single-turn primary for all the coils through which it is threaded, the wire causes a voltage to be induced in the multiturn secondary coils associated with the core. This voltage operates a gate to place a mark on the corresponding output code marking lead. The translation for any equipment number may be changed by simply threading the associated wire through different coils. Many wires may be threaded through the same cores. The wires thus act as individual coding devices and the cores as a reading equipment common to all coding elements. Since the translation in this case is from the equipment number to the directory number of a calling subscriber, it is abbreviated as an EN-to-DN translation. The above coding method was proposed by T. L. Dimond of the Bell Telephone Laboratories and the system is known as the **Dimond ring** translator. It is quite flexible and is useful for either DN-to-EN or EN-to-DN translations.

In the handling of toll calls, translation is an extremely important feature, especially where the networks are large

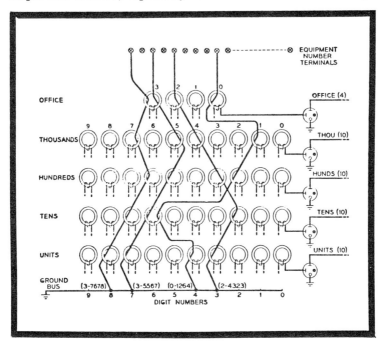

Fig. 5-7. The Dimond ring core translator. (Bell Systems Technical Journal.)

and complicated. In large toll switching systems, the ingenious use of translation makes possible the realization of many important features within reasonable economic limits. Beyond the typical central office requirements covered above, switching instructions must be provided for interswitch paths and intertoll routes of the preferred combination as well as alternate route indications. The output code of the translator of a large toll crossbar exchange consists of many different numbers in various bases, providing the information required to complete the long-distance call. Direct distance dialing has, of course, placed additional requirements upon toll exchange translators. Translators suitable for toll center switching present special design problems because of the large number of codes they must handle. Punched cards which interrupt light beams in various patterns are used in some toll switching systems to provide the translation function.

Translation and coding are closely related and, needless to say, many codes can be utilized. However, it is sufficient here to mention one called the two-out-of-five code. Since there are 10 digits available from the telephone dial, it is necessary to have a code with at least 5 elements to provide 10 self-checking combinations. This code uses 10 combinations of 5 elements taken 2 at a time, as its name implies. In Table 5-1 the relationship of this code to the dial digits is shown. The elements of the code are designated 0, 1, 2, 4, and 7. Thus, the combinations are all additive to the corresponding digit, except 4 and 7, which do not add to zero.

Table 5-1. The Two-Out-of-Five Code.			
Digit	Two-out-of five 0-1-2-4-7	Digit	Two-out-of-five 0-1-2-4-7
1	0-1	6	2-4
2	0-2	7	0-7
3	1-2	8	1-7
4	0-4	9	2-7
5	1-4	0	4-7

In practice each digit is represented by two out of five available frequencies, and in one application enables the marker to determine the equipment number to which a connection should be extended.

Registers

Although the basic purpose of the **register** is to store the subscriber dialed digits in a form which can be utilized for the control of the speech-path switching network, the term has been used loosely to include the translation function as well in some cases. Also, the register has sometimes been related to the term, **sender** as in **register-sender.** Here it refers to the function of not only storing information but sending it on for control purposes.

The register was the first component to appear in the development of common-control systems. Both the early rotary and panel switching systems utilized registers and register-senders which included the translation function. The componentry of registers has taken a variety of forms during the past 65 years. The major differences in the early designs of rotary and panel systems was due to the methods of controlling the selectors and the different access of these systems. Both used revertive pulsing rather than marking to control the selection process. As the selectors progressed they sent back pulses, which were counted by the sender or register. When a selector reached the desired position, the sender opened the pulsing circuit stopping it.

The block diagram of a register with pulse detector and counter circuits as used in a wired logic electronic exchange is shown in Fig. 5-8. It is seen that after signal processing by electronic methods, the pulse information is stored in reed relays.

Electrical Marking and Markers

The simple function of electrical marking can be illustrated rather simply as it is applied to rotary switches. For instance, in the indirect control of an EMD motorswitch the group steps are electrically marked in one method as shown in Fig. 5-9. The dial pulses operate a stepping relay in the motorswitch's relay set. The contact points in the relay set are connected to the contacts in the switch multiple, which represent the beginning of the dialed decade (the group step). As the motorswitch rotates, its fourth switch arm tests the marked contact on which the switch is then stopped. After selection of the marked decade, the motorswitch begins to

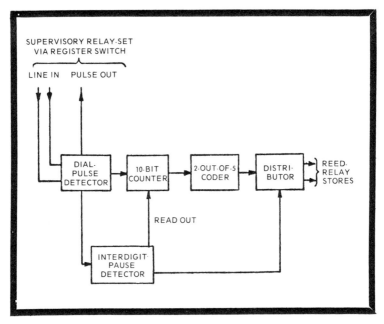

Fig. 5-8. Pulse-detector and counter circuits in a register.

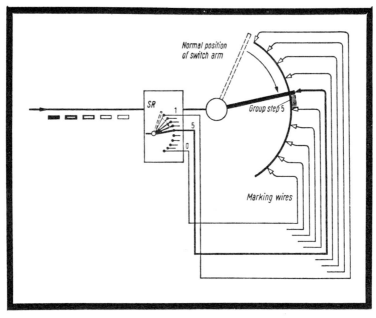

Fig. 5-9. Electrical marking on the EMD motorswitch by stepping relay.
(Siemens Akiengesellschaft.)

hunt within the group step. Rather than using the stepping relay to set the marking of the EMD motorswitches, it is usually preferable to do so through a control set that concentrates the control elements of several switches for greater economy.

In a modern electronic exchange using wired logic, as in the British TXE-2, marking plays about the same role as in crossbar exchanges. Each connection through the speech-path switches consists of three or four wires or leads—the two speech wires, a hold wire or sleeve lead to hold the network path during a conversation, and a fourth wire if required for signaling. The marking function is combined with an **interrogating function**, with both using electrical and electronic techniques. The interrogating function involves simultaneous inspection of all switching stages from end to end of a desired connection—connections of subscriber to register, calling subscriber to called subscriber, and register to auxiliary equipment. Since these interrogating operations can take place only one at a time at each exchange, they must be done rapidly. In the case of the TXE-2 about four interrogations per second are made during the busy hour. Interrogation involves the sampling of potentials on the hold wires of switch inlets and outlets to determine whether they are free or busy. Voltage-discriminating circuits are used to accomplish these operations.

Although larger exchanges require the use of several interrogators distributed throughout the switching network, the TXE-2 switching network is served by one interrogator which is duplicated to insure continuity of service. A common voltage-discriminating element per interrogating function, which is relay switched to indicate inlets and outlets during interrogation, is used in this exchange. Figure 5-10 shows the method used. The access relays are operated from marking relays associated with the network terminal points between which a connection is required, and these are operated by signals maintained continuously by the control system for the duration of the interrogation. Different terminal points require interrogation of different switch inlets and outlets through the operation of different access relays. The discriminating circuit indicates free when a positive potential is observed, and busy when a negative potential is present. The negative potential is produced when hold current is flowing in the crosspoint relay coils. When a switch is removed

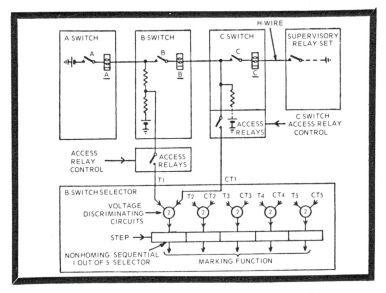

Fig. 5-10. The interrogation function in the TXE-2 exchange.

from the rack, the positive bias potential will be absent, producing an effect similar to a busy condition.

In a typical call-selection operation of the TXE-2 (Fig. 5-10) the common control first instructs a C-switch selector to choose a C switch, which has a free supervisory relay set connected to it. The C switch access-relay contacts then close and the B-C link test wires (CT 1-5) are connected to the path-choice equipment (B-switch selector). At the same time, the five A-B links associated with the subscriber are also extended to the B-switch selector. The path-choice equipment then chooses complementary A-B and B-C links—that is, one complete connection between the subscriber and the selected C switch. This selection is accomplished by a nonhoming, sequential, one-out-of-five selector which consists of interconnected diode gates and memory elements. When the selection has been made and signaled to the marker, the selector takes one step, which is to insure that if the selected connection is faulty a different path can be selected when an automatic second attempt is made to establish the call.

Once a path is selected, the next step is to operate the reed-relay crosspoints to establish it. The process in this case is defined as the **marking function**. However, by some definitions the interrogation function just described is also considered to be a part of the marker. In any case the marking equipment needs to know the identities of the two points to be connected through the network for which it is responsible. One point will be a calling or called subscriber, junction, etc., and the other will be a supervisory or link circuit chosen by the path-choice equipment. The marking of the path to be switched is shown in Fig. 5-11. The selected supervisory relay set is marked by the common control equipment, and accordingly the supervisory relay set applies positive battery potential to the hold wire. The line circuit, having been marked, has ground applied to the mark wire of its A-switch crosspoint relays. Positive potentials are applied to the mark wires of the B switch and C switch by the selector and access circuits. Thus, the C-switch crosspoint operates in the C switch, followed by the B-switch crosspoint and the A-switch crosspoint. The operation of the A-switch crosspoint relay replaces the marking ground with negative potential. The initial end-to-end holding potential is thus 100 volts, but the positive battery is subsequently removed, leaving the crosspoint relays holding in series to a ground at the supervisory relay set. The supervisory relay set operates the K relay in the line circuit by applying a ground to the signal wire, thereby disconnecting the LR relay from the line. The line is extended from the supervisory relay set into the register by means of a full-availability register switch. The

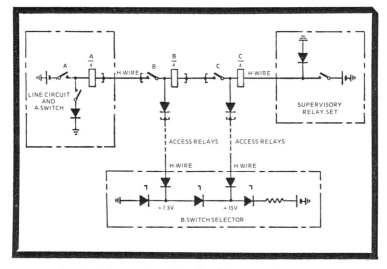

Fig. 5-11. The marking function in the TXE-2 exchange

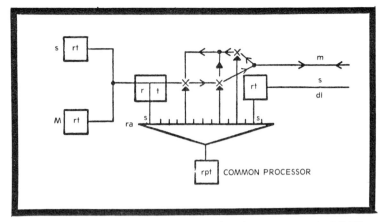

Fig. 5-12. Basic operations in common stored-program control. (IEE—Conference Publications No. 52.)

register supplies line-feed current, returns dial tone, and awaits dial pulses. These operations by the supervisory relay are not shown in Fig. 5-10.

The interrogation and marking operations described here are comparable to those in a crossbar switching system, except that the holding relays would be on the crossbar switch instead of in the reed relays. The programing of an exchange with a Dimond ring translator is described in Chapter 8.

COMMON STORED-PROGRAM CONTROL

Using Flowers' notation a basic common stored-program exchange is diagramed in Fig. 5-12. Subscriber lines carrying message and signal information enter a receive-transmit apparatus, which can be accessed by a common processor (rpt) over a random-access (ra) switch. This switch is "random access" in that every item of rt equipment and switch control equipment has an address by which it can be accessed by the common processor at any time. The exchange switches carry only messages from the subscribers. From each junction group to another exchange there is a data link (dl) over which coded signals are passed to control the continuing of the message path in the other exchange. The data links are accessed via a random-access switch. The operation of the exchange consists of each receive-transmit unit being accessed frequently to determine its condition. Memorizing of the previous history of the rt units and switches takes place within the common processor. By the selective accessing of switch control and rt units, the switches are operated and the signals transmitted as the determined states of the equipment indicate. By examining each rt unit more frequently than its signaling condition can change, any need for the common control equipment to anticipate events is eliminated. By its operation the common stored-program processor eliminates all logic processes from the equipment distributed throughout the exchange and places all decision-making and controlling functions in the common processor. Thus, the common stored-program processor is the ultimate development of common control in that all of the processing is concentrated in a common processor with none remaining distributed throughout the exchange as has been the case with all prior common control systems.

It appears on the surface that the removal of all processing from equipments in trunks and junctions, which also removes the need for signaling through the exchange switches and removes all signaling equipment from trunks and junctions, would result in considerable economies. However, the simple concept of lodging all control functions in a common processor leads to some complications which shift the economics in the other direction. First, it is necessary to duplicate the common processor and the random-access switch because the whole exchange is dependent upon them. Also, an elaborate means of fault-detection is required to insure that even the duplicated equipment will be in service if needed. Second, the receive-transmit equipment at the exchange end of each line must be capable of sending and receiving all of the signals needed by the peripheral equipment, which involves a considerable amount of apparatus per line. Such an arrangement would be far too expensive, so it is necessary to transfer as many receive-transmit functions as possible to less numerous equipments, using the exchange line-terminal equipment to detect only the calling signal and using concentration switches to connect receive-transmit switches as required. As a result some signals must remain in the line-terminal equipments to be handled by receive-transmit equipment as shown in Fig. 5-13.

Another complication is that due to the large number of operations to be performed by the processor, it can dwell for only a few microseconds on each equipment which it must scan. This is too short a time for any control or signaling

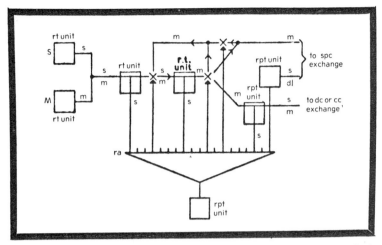

Fig. 5-13. Basic operations in semi-stored-program common control.
(IEE—Conference Publications No. 52.)

operations to be completed. Solutions to this problem involve slowing the scan rate, or giving instructions on successive scans for a sufficient number of times to be effective, or giving instruction only to the receive-transmit units and letting them carry out the instruction. All of these solutions may require that processing functions be removed from the common processor and be distributed into the exchange. Another difficulty is that the common processor can give instructions for signals and operations to be carried out, but it cannot by itself execute the orders. As a result, receive-transmit units employing bistable and monostable circuits must be operated by the common processor. These in turn control gates, relays, etc. to operate switches, apply signals, and perform other functions. It is for these reasons that stored-program control has not found its way into all levels of exchange switching. However, stored-program-control systems are being installed in considerable quantities in the U.S. as large exchanges, and the benefits of computer processing in other facilities are being realized by the Bell System.

SIGNALING METHODS

Signaling for the purpose of controlling exchange switching falls into two categories: (1) signaling between subscribers and their exchange and (2) signaling between exchanges. Within each category there are two main classes— **address signals** and **supervisory signals.** The former direct the call to its proper destination and assure that it is charged to the correct subscriber. The latter convey information about the progress of a call. For example, when the calling subscriber lifts his handset off hook, a connect signal is generated; when the called subscriber lifts his handset, an answer signal is generated; and when either subscriber places his handset back on hook, a disconnect signal is generated. In the control of communications switching systems, one is primarily concerned with address signaling because it has the main effect upon the switching network in making the desired connection between subscribers. However, the supervisory signaling is essential to the proper progress of the calls.

Signaling Between the Subscriber and the Exchange

When a subscriber initiates a call by using a rotary dial, he generates loop-disconnect pulsing at a rate of approximately 10 pulses per second. Thus, each dial pulse has a period of about 100 msec, with the break interval about 60 to 64 percent of the total pulse period. These intervals vary slightly in the telephone instruments used in different countries as well as within manufacturing tolerances. For instance, in England the break interval is about 66 percent of the total period of 100 msec. As shown in Fig. 5-14 there is an inter-digital pause about four times as long as the dial pulse duration due to the windup time and lost motion of the dial mechanism.

Rotary dial telephone instruments have been available since the end of the 19th century and are still widely used. Although the multifrequency signaling of pushbutton telephone instruments is preferred for operation with elec-

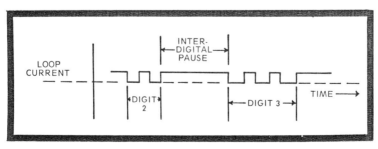

Fig. 5-14. Loop-disconnect pulse signaling or ordinary rotary telephone dial.

tronic exchanges, it is necessary to design such exchanges to accommodate rotary-dial signaling as well.

Multifrequency Signaling by the Subscriber

A telephone number can be keyed about twice as fast as it can be dialed by a rotary unit. Keying is made possible in pushbutton telephone instruments by having each button key the transmission of two audio-frequency signals simultaneously. At the central office exchange a receiver accepts and translates these tones for storage in registers to perform essentially the same functions as the loop-disconnect pulses mentioned above. Table 5-2 shows the relationship between the digit to be transmitted and the frequency combinations which are sent. Signals of 770 Hz and 1336 Hz are transmitted for the digit 5, for example.

Table 5-2. Frequencies Used in Multifrequency Signaling.

	HIGH TONE		
LOW TONE	1205 Hz	1336 Hz	1447 Hz
697 Hz	1	2	3
770 Hz	4	5	6
852 Hz	7	8	9
941 Hz	*	0	#

Encoders with keyboards of the type shown in Fig. 5-15 incorporate the necessary circuits to generate the frequencies indicated adjacent to each button. Multifrequency signaling of this type is referred to as **in-band signaling**, because it is within the voice frequency range of the transmitted message.

Audio-Frequency Signaling between Exchanges

For signaling between exchanges (Fig. 5-16) both single— and multifrequency in-band and out-of-band systems are employed. The International Telephone and Telegraph Consultative Committee (CCITT) has recommended 2280 Hz for single-frequency in-band signaling. However, other frequencies are used for SF signals, for example, 2600 Hz. It is common practice to use out-of-band signaling in carrier systems serving short haul toll circuits. Examples are Lenkurt's use of 3400 and 3550 Hz and the Bell System's use of 3700 Hz in its O, N, and ON carrier systems. In the case of single-frequency in-band signaling it is necessary to take special precautions to achieve immunity from speech-signal interference. By taking into account the differences in the characteristics of speech frequencies and single audio frequencies at the signal receiver, satisfactory performance is realized.

In the case of multifrequency interoffice signaling, the CCITT has recommended systems No. 4 and No. 5. System No. 4 uses the frequencies of 2040 and 2400 Hz for register and line signals. The register signals use a binary code and are transmitted in four steps. System No. 5 is for use with semiautomatic traffic on trans-Atlantic cables. Line signals are at frequencies of 2400 and 2600 Hz, and register signals are transmitted via a two-out-of-six code of frequencies. These cover the range from 700 to 1700 Hz and are spaced 200 Hz apart. Actually, standardization has not been achieved in various countries and several other frequency combinations

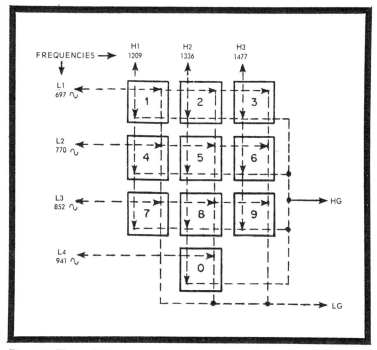

Fig. 5-15. The multifrequency signaling generated by pushbutton phones.

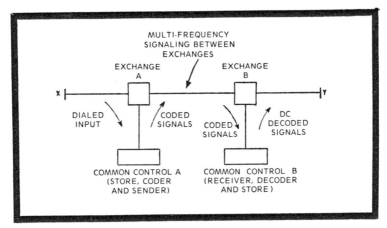

Fig. 5-16. Multifrequency signaling between exchanges is common.

are in use. A considerable amount of low frequency ac and dc signaling is also used between exchanges.

DC Signaling between Exchanges

Switching offices may convert subscriber-dialed signals to other forms, such as **E-lead**, **M-lead**, and **battery-ground** forms to operate over greater distances than is possible with loop-disconnect methods. Other forms, such as duplex (DX) signaling utilize both dc and ac. In such methods the ac signal is often out of band, below the voice frequency range. Direct-current signaling is often used in PABXs, where it has the advantage of low cost in signal production (by diodes and switch contacts) and simple detection by relay circuits. Unfortunately, dc signaling can not be passed beyond the local network—at least without translation to some other form—as can audio frequencies in the multifrequency ranges mentioned above.

Data-Link Junction Signaling

The increasing installation of common-processor exchanges, especially in the U.S., has emphasized the need for data-links between them to handle signaling in the future. Data links can provide unlimited signaling capacity at a low cost per junction where large groups of junctions are involved. An example of data link signaling is found in Bell System's

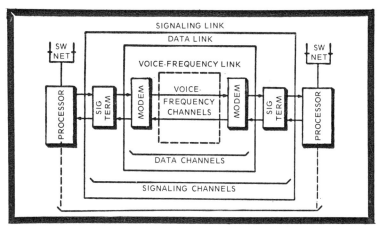

Fig. 5-17. Common channel interoffice signaling system (CCIS). (IEE ISS Record.)

common channel interoffice signaling system (CCIS). The signaling terminal interfaces with the electronic processor of the switching office and with a modem for transmitting and receiving signals to and from the distant office. A voice-frequency link can be used, with some conditioning, to operate at a minimum of 2400 bits per second and a maximum of 4800 bits per second. Another plan would utilize a digital link, eliminating the need for a modem. Signaling information generated in the processor is transmitted in parallel form to the signaling terminal, which in turn tramsits the information to the modem in serial form using a 28-bit word, of which 20 bits are data and 8 bits are for error checking.

The CCIS system is very compatible with the CCITT system No. 6, which is also a separate-channel data-signaling system. As shown in Fig. 5-17, a data link connects the processors of exchanges A and B to handle a signal of about the same format as that of the CCIS. The signaling and message paths are completely separated, which enables the processor and data channels to handle signals relating to calls on speech circuits not switched at a given center. Known as **quasi associated signaling**, this concept enables a network to operate without having data links between every pair of exchanges and provides important economies.

Order-wire signaling, where all signals for a group of junctions (which carry only messages) are carried over one bothway circuit, has many of the characteristics of a data link and can be a viable substitute in some cases.

Modern Step-by-Step and Rotary Exchanges

6

The operation of step-by-step Strowger switches and various type of rotary switches was described in Chapter 4. However, the manner in which such switches are utilized in switching networks was not shown there. Since all forms of rectangular and rotary switches are old in concept and design and no longer the subject of new development, it might be thought that little of a new or modern nature could be ascribed to systems using such designs. Nevertheless, millions of subscriber lines are still being served by Strowger or rotary switches around the world, while new services such as direct distance dialing (subscriber trunk dialing) have appeared on an international basis. Consequently, it has become essential to either replace or modernize step-by-step and rotary switching systems. This has led to the introduction of new common-control techniques and equipment—particularly in the form of register-translators, which in many cases are either completely or substantially electronic in design.

Basic Step-by-Step Switching Systems

The basic functional switching elements of step-by-step exchanges are classified as: line-finders, selectors, and connectors (final selectors).

Prior to 1928 each subscriber line had its own **line switch,** but since then the **line-finder** technique has minimized the equipment associated with each individual line. Analogous to a manual switchboard operator's arm and plug, the line-finder switch literally reaches up to find the calling line. A small pool of line-finder switches, common to a group of lines, is available so that one automatically finds the calling subscriber's line when its handset is removed from the cradle of a telephone in the group. The calling subscriber's line is thus extended to the succeeding switch (a selector or connector).

The principle of the line-finder is the reverse of that of the line switch, although the purpose of each is to concentrate traffic on a smaller number of numerical switches than lines. In the line-switch system, each subscriber's line is connected directly to a line switch which selects an idle numerical switch; while in the line-finder system, a finder switch—directly connected to a numerical switch—seeks and connects with the subscriber's line. Strowger switches and rotary switches are both employed in line-finder systems. The simplest form of line-finder system is that employing a nonhoming type of rotary switch. The subscribers' lines are directly connected to the bank contacts of the switch and, therefore, the number of lines which may be served by a group of finder switches is limited by the number of contacts in the bank level. A system more generally used utilizes both rotary and Strowger switches and permits the use of 200-line groups.

As shown in Fig. 6-1, the **selecting** function is the next in the interconnecting network. Here the caller's dial controls the first or vertical motion of a Strowger switch, which selects the equipment group having access to the called line. Then the switch shaft rotates automatically, hunting idle equipment within the chosen group. Typically, all but the last two or terminal-selecting digits of a telephone directory number operate the selectors. Thus, a 1000-line central office uses selectors for hundred-selection; for example, if one calls the

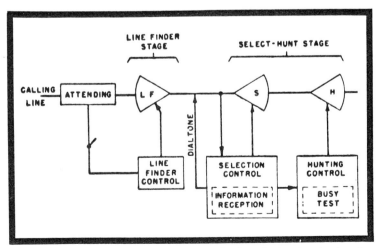

Fig. 6-1. The selection function follows the line finder in step-by-step systems.

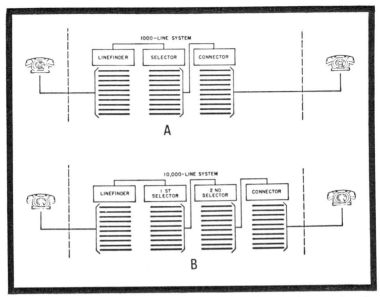

Fig. 6-2. The arrangement of line-finders, selectors, and connectors in 1,000- and 10,000-line step-by-step systems.

telephone number 345, when 3 is dialed a selector selects the 300 group. Thus, a 10,000-line central office requires two ranks of selectors—one for thousand selection and another for hundred selection.

Following the selecting function in the step-by-step system is the **connecting** or **final selecting function,** where a Strowger switch performs operations analogous to that of a manual-switchboard operator's arm, front plug, ringing key, etc. The typical connector switch has access to 100 lines. The last digits dialed by the caller control the connector. Because automatic switch boards are inherently multiple switch-boards, the connector tests whether the called line is busy. If the called line is busy, the connector sends a busy tone to the calling party. If the called line is idle, the connector rings out on that line. When the called party answers, the connector cuts off the ringing and supplies transmitter current to both the calling and called parties. When both parties hang up, the connector releases itself and other equipment used during the conversation.

A virtually self-sufficient switch, the connector supplies busy tone, ringing current, transmitter current, and discon-nect control. If the exchange does not require selectors, a complete central office can be built on only line-finders and connectors. Outside the U.S. the connector switch is referred to as the final selector. The arrangement of line-finders, selectors, and connectors in a typical 1000-line system is shown in Fig. 6-2A. In a 10,000-line system an additional selector is required as shown in Fig. 6-2B.

Direct Control in a Basic Step-by-Step System

In a direct-control system—sometimes referred to as a direct-progressive-control system—the selecting switches of the interconnecting network are under the direct control of the subscriber, operating directly from the pulses dialed into them. Thus, signals representing the directory number not only drive the appropriate switching mechanism, but control interoffice signaling as well, within limited areas. The functions of receiving pulses, controlling selection, performing busy tests, hunting, returning busy tone, and cutting through are all built into each step-by-step switch. Also, many specialized switches are provided in each exchange to handle dial tone, ringing, talking, battery, and supervision connections. During the talking condition, all of the various selection and hunting functions and many of the auxiliary functions are kept out of service because the switches are fully occupied in handling the message connections.

Despite the fact that such direct control operation has the inflexibility of requiring that the subscriber lines be located on the switches of the connector stages in strict correspondence with their directory numbers, direct-control step-by-step systems are very attractive for certain exchange applications. This is especially true in the case of smaller installations, where they can be quite economical and efficient. Step-by-step systems have handled most of the rural and small town switching in the U.S. for decades and have been used in many small and medium installations throughout the world. Although direct-control step-by-step systems have been installed in some large metropolitan areas, some disadvantages become more apparent in the larger exchange applications. These are the need for considerable spare capacity to provide a satisfactory grade of service due to the fact that the systems must hunt for and choose an idle trunk in an early stage of the network without having determined the possibility of blocking due to links being busy in later stages, the need for a relatively large number of switching stages, and the inflexibility in trunk assignments due to the necessity of conforming to the office code digits, which are part of the directory number.

The routing of a call under the direct control of the subscriber requires the use of direct trunking, which is uneconomical in a metropolitan network due to the fluctuations in traffic volume. An excessive number of idle trunks can be avoided through the use of tandem switching centers, but such operation cannot be accommodated with direct trunking. The simplest way to overcome this problem without installing completely different switching systems was to dissociate the fixed office-code numbering system from the trunking system and to substitute translated **directing numbers** for the office codes, thereby permitting the switch trains to be designed for a more efficient use of both switches and trunks. A system designed to accomplish this became known as a **director**.

The dissociation of the telephone directory office code from the trunking system offered several advantages in addition to permitting interoffice trunk routing in the most economical manner. It took advantage of the efficiency obtainable by the use of larger trunk groups, provided a simple means of rerouting calls as traffic conditions change, and served in facilitating the transition from manual to step-by-step operation. Also, the choice of office designations was simplified, since trunk routing no longer affected their selection.

The Director System

To effect economies through the use of translated directing digits in the exchange trunk plant, the director system was introduced in 1923. It was a successful compromise between step-by-step and common-control principles, since the directors (a form of electromechanical register-translators) were designed to work with the existing Strowger equipment. Figure 6-3 illustrates the elementary principles of the system. The subscriber, on lifting his handset, is connected through a relay set at the first code selector to a uniselector, known as an A-digit hunter. This hunting switch finds a free A-digit selector. The first digit dialed steps the selector to the director group level required and by automatic rotation a disengaged director is found.

The director receives and registers the remaining two digits of the route code and the four digits of the numerical code. As soon as the route code has been received (after the third digit), the director starts to send out the translated code. The first digit operates the first code selector, which hunts in the usual manner in the selected level. The remaining digits of the translated code operate the succeeding selectors, which extend the call to the destination exchange. After the translated route code, the director sends out the numerical code without translation. The impulses operate numerical selectors of the usual type, which complete the connection to the called subscriber in the exchange to which the call has been extended.

As soon as the director has completed its sending functions it releases. The A-digit switch also releases. The calling line is

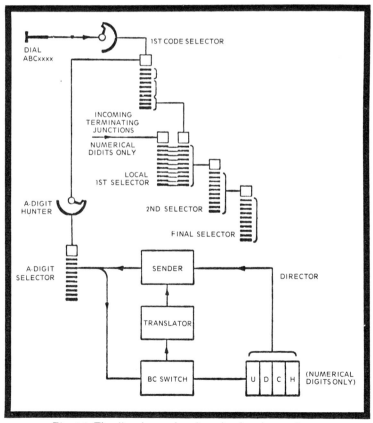

Fig. 6-3. The director system in a step-by-step exchange.

connected at the circuit of the first code selector to the established connection, which is thereafter controlled by the calling subscriber as though it had been set up in the usual way. The A-digit selector and the director immediately become available for other calls.

Advantages of the Director System. In this way, the principle of code translation was introduced into the British telephone system. Instead of the subscriber having to dial every digit needed to route a call, it was provided that he should merely actuate an internal reference device which would seek out the full code and translate from his key. This enabled the establishment of a uniform code system over the whole of the London area and the consequent extension of tandem switching for the increasingly complex routing patterns within the metropolis.

So the "pure" Strowger principle of direct pulsing was modified. The step-by-step system, designed to eliminate the need for translation services of human operators, had been changed to operate with machine intervention in interpreting the exchange code. A limited start had been made toward a system of register-translation.

Disadvantages of the Director System. The maximum number of director groups is 8 (since 1 and 0 are not used for director selection) and each group translates up to 100 codes. A register-translation system not employing the A-digit for group selection (i.e., one translating all the dialed information) would enable more codes to be dealt with and would offer greater director availability.

Furthermore, the director system necessarily involves an extension of tandem switching, which in turn may mean the higher incidence of lost calls—failure of switching contacts being the major cause of imperfect connections. The problem is rather smaller nowadays, with the improvement of modern switches and their reliability, but may still be a factor to be considered in the planning of amendments to a network.

Finally, since the directors are a compromise insertion in the established routing pattern, they involve the acceptance of former routing methods. Only the destination exchange is found by the directors, the 4-digit numerical code being retained at the local routing stage. If the desired route is not available, the system lacks sufficient flexibility to reroute the call another way, so the connection is lost.

The Effect of New Services

The introduction of direct distance dialing—or as it is called in England and some other parts of the world, subscriber trunk dialing—brought new problems for step-by-step exchanges. In particular in England, where step-by-step is the national system, the need arose for register-translator equipment that went beyond the director. Both a national and a local type of equipment had to be added to the system. The national device, called a controlling register-translator, was required to hold the complete national number as dialed and a large proportion of the national routing information. Such large controllers communicate with each other and cooperate in the routing of a national call through sequential areas in the same way that human operators call on each other in a manual service. The local device, called an incoming register-translator, is designed to process signals entering a smaller local area, whether from an adjacent system or over the national trunk network. Of course, it is smaller than the controlling register-translator. Provision for call-charging is included in both the national and local equipments.

Those who wished to extend step-by-step exchanges for direct distance dialing in the U.S. were confronted with similar problems and register-senders and register-translators were also introduced here by companies such as Automatic Electric and Stromberg-Carlson, who had been supplying step-by-step equipment to the independent telephone companies. It was necessary to add such equipment to step-by-step installations in large metropolitan areas first, but the demand for extended area service in smaller communities required the installation of such equipment there as well.

A further development is Touch-Tone or pushbutton dialing, which appeared in the 1960's. It also required the modification of step-by-step installations if they were to provide such service. Actually, this service could be accommodated by either register-sender equipment or equipment added only to provide specifically for it.

Controlling Register-Translator

A controlling register-translator (Fig. 6-4) may be considered as composed of four sections as follows:

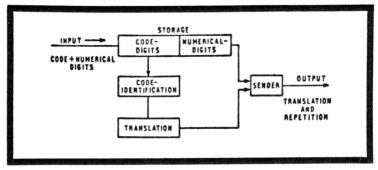

Fig. 6-4. The basic sections in a controlling register-translator.

1. A storage section, in which the received information at the input is stored, digit by digit.

2. A code-identification section, in which the received code is distinguished from all other possible codes

3. A translation section, in which all the required translators are available

4. A sending section, which is required to transmit charging and routing information derived from the translation, and also to repeat some or all of the original information held in the storage section.

A typical British electromechanical translator (Fig. 6-5) operates in the following manner. The register applies start and mark conditions to the translator, which is common to a group of registers, when the first three digits have been received and stored. The register-finder hunts for, and switches to the calling register. Simultaneous or overlapping demands from registers served by the same translator are dealt with in the order in which they appear on the register-finder banks.

When found by the translator, a group of relays in the register is operated to couple the equipments together. The three digits stored in the register are marked into the translator and identified by a group of relays. In most cases, translation is possible from a 3-digit code, with the translator operating a translation-relay appropriate to the particular combination of routing and charging information. Following this two digits are returned to the register. One indicates which digits of the stored national number should be sent following the routing digits, and the other indicates the call-charging rate. If three digits are insufficient to permit translation, a translation relay is not operated but a signal is returned to the register indicating that another try should be made on the receipt of the fourth, or the fourth and fifth digits.

Upon receipt of the charging-digit and the sending instruction, the register releases the translator, which can then deal with demands from other registers. Only one translation digit is returned to the register upon each demand after the register has indicated to the translator which digit is required. The fee or charging digit is sent by the register to the access relay set which selects the appropriate metering rate. Succeeding digits returned to the translator are for routing and are sent by the register, via the access relay set, to step the trunk selectors. When the final routing digit is reached, the translator sends an additional signal with it to denote that it is the last digit. Upon making a demand to the translator, each register checks the delay in receiving a reply against a 6-second time pulse. If no reply is received within this period, it is assumed that a fault exists; the translator is switched out of service and an alarm is sounded.

The translator uses a cross-connection field (C) on which translations are set up by soldering connections, which are changed from time to time because of the need to make additions and changes to the translations. A second cross-

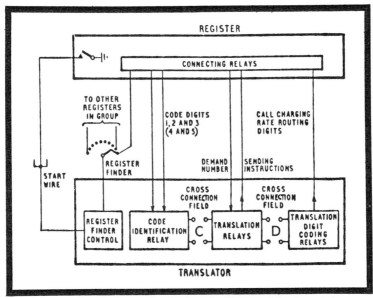

Fig. 6-5. An electromechanical controlling register-translator.

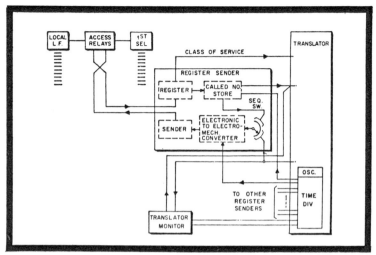

Fig. 6-6. Automatic electric's series 100 director (register-translator) connected to an existing step-by-step exchange.

connection field (D) is used to determine the code used to transfer information from the translator to the register. The code may be a two-out-of-six code, which is inherently self-checking, or a system based on binary signaling on four wires supplemented by two additional wires for checking purposes.

Automatic Electric Translators

Early in the 1960's the Automatic Electric Company introduced their Series 100 directors, which are really register-translators designed to cope with essentially the same problems in step-by-step systems as the equipments which were installed in England. These Automatic Electric register-translators are electromechanical in their register-sender portion and electronic in their translator section. As shown in the block diagram of Fig. 6-6, the access relays are added between the local line finder and the first selector switches of existing step-by-step exchanges without modification of existing switches or shelves. By 1965 the 100 series director was offered in two types—the type 101 director for local offices and a newer type 102 for toll offices. However, the circuitry of both was similar, with electromechanical register-senders and electronic translators. In the register-sender the dialed digits are stored in reed relays mounted on printed cards with a capacity of two digits per card. The storage system utilizes a two-out-of-five parity code for error detection. Translated routing information is not stored, but is sent directly from the translator. An open loop to the selector is provided to absorb the first dialed digit. By appropriate strapping, the register-sender can be arranged to repeat the first dialed digit to the route selector; subsequent dialed digits can be repeated under control of the translator.

The type 101 register-translator provides for early release, if the dialed number indicates that it is not required. Then succeeding digits are dialed directly into the step-by-step switch train. Early release is a means for reducing the number of register-senders required in an office by allowing certain types of calls to be completed on a direct-dial basis. All calls to be completed within the local office provide for early release of the register-sender. Access equipment for the register-senders consists of access relays (1 for each line finder), link-finder control (1 for each 100 access relays), and crosspoint relay-switch link-finders (two per register-sender). The control circuit has the capacity to control 100 access circuits into 12 register-senders. The type 101 register-translator is for use with local central-office step-by-step systems and in such a role adds sufficient common-control features to provide for extended area service in the form of direct distance dialing, operation with pushbutton telephones, trunking to offices requiring multifrequency signaling, and the maximum use of selector-level assignments.

A Newer-Type Register-Translator

The type 102 register-translator plays a somewhat similar role to the controlling register-translator which is associated with toll centers (group switching centers) in England. It was developed to aid in the completion of out-going calls from toll switchboards to higher level exchanges and to aid in the completion of incoming calls through the intertoll network from class 4-or-higher-level offices to class 5 offices. The main functions of the register-sender are: (1) to receive the digital signaling from an operator or sender in the preceding office (2) to provide storage and routing on the basis of the information received; and (3) to serve as the communication link to the translator. Signaling to and from the equipment can be either dial pulses or two-out-of-six multifrequency signals.

115

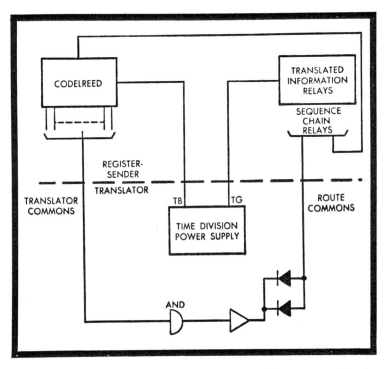

Fig. 6-7. Extension of reed-relay contacts to a highway connecting the register-sender to the translator in an Automatic Electric type 102 register-translator.

The register-sender can receive either of these signals from trunks or operators, but the use of MF signals from the toll board is preferred because it greatly simplifies the work of the operator. The equipment outpulses a prearranged number of dial-pulse digits to seize the trunk routes through its associated selectors. However, once the toll trunk is seized, the director can shift to MF signals if the distant office is arranged to receive MF signaling.

Up to 14 digits can be stored in the register-sender, where they are changed to a two-out-of-five code and stored in reed relays. Figure 6-7 shows how the reed-relay contacts are extended to a highway connecting the register-sender to the translator, which consists of logic circuits (mostly ANDs, ORs, inverters, and amplifiers) and route diodes that meet the various translation requirements. The translator contains a program panel, which is used to interconnect the various logic circuits within the system and to allow for changing the translations. Normally two translators are provided per office, one of which is a duplicate for the sake of reliability. One translator can handle up to 100 register-senders on a time-division basis. Because the translator is an electronic type, the register-translator can handle such special features as **digit deletion, digit prefixing,** and **alternate routing.** (These terms are defined in the glossary.)

Normally in toll operation, more than three digits must be translated. If the translator has a number of routes to an area code, it can perform a 6-digit translation on the area and office codes. Six code gates in the **home area toll** equipment rack of the translator provide for 6-digit translations. If a 6-digit translation is required, the second set of three digits and class-of-service marks are presented to the **foreign area toll** equipment rack of the translator. There are 80 route treatments possible in this rack, but any number of codes can be translated. One of the outstanding features of the type 102 register-translator is its ability to select alternate routes by means of its translator. If the high-usage group to which it is first routed is busy, the call is then routed to another trunk group. This function demands highly flexible code conversions, and in some cases, the ability to prefix digits ahead of the called office code.

The Minisender

Since register-translators are added mainly to step-by-step offices already in existence, it is obvious that equipment occupying the minimum amount of space would be highly desirable especially in small offices. With a floor space requirement of only 8 square feet a very compact equipment called the Minisender has been introduced by Stromberg-Carlson. Although referred to as a sender, it is actually a register-translator for small step-by-step offices of up to 1000 lines in the smallest version and up to 2000 lines with an added 3-foot cabinet. It performs essentially the functions already described. Although it has separate electromechanical and electronic equipment bays, the former contains only the access equipment and space for optional features while the latter contains two complete electronic register-translators. Up to 10 calls can be processed simultaneously with the 2 bays of equipment and up to 20 calls with the addition of an optional electromechanical bay.

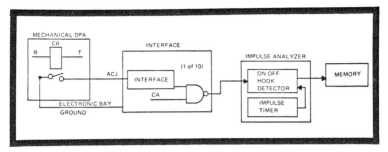

Fig. 6-8. The use of cell address in the Stromberg-Carlson Minisender
(Stromberg-Carlson Corp.).

The register-sender, which can store up to 12 subscriber-dialed digits, has a special reflexing arrangement which permits it to handle up to 15 subscriber-dialed digits. Up to 3 of the first digits can be acted upon and then erased from memory, leaving a storage space for 12 additional digits. For example, a 3-digit direct distance dialing access code can be erased from memory leaving the register-sender with a capability of storing up to 12 additional digits. The electronic translator section is capable of examining the digit train and then providing appropriate call-routing information or instructions to perform special functions prior to the outpulsing of the dialed digits. For a particular code or group of codes, the translator can provide routing instructions for one primary route and up to three alternate routes.

The register-translator is a time-division multiplex device that allots sequential time periods for up to 10 simultaneous calls. The time period for any particular call is referred to as the **cell address** time. This period recurs every 2.8 msec and is of sufficient duration to permit storage of thirty-two 4-bit binary words into memory, as needed, to process the call. "Cell address," as referred to in this case, signifies the gating or steering signal used for any one specific call during the process time. The on-to-off hook transitions for any 1 of 10 dial-pulse acceptors are presented through an interface circuit to a logic NAND gate where they are combined with the cell address. This is because there are 10 cells in the dynamic recirculating memory. Cell address represents the time allotted to a particular dial-pulse acceptor (DPA). Therefore, about 357 times a second or every 2.8 msec, cell address appears to determine the presence of a ground or open from relay CB of the DPA (Fig. 6-8). With standard dial pulses the

118

impulse analyzer is allowed to sample the off-hook bus many times during a normal impulse of a digit. These intervals are presented to the on/off hook detector, which operates in conjunction with an electronic timing clock. For any cell the impulse analyzer, via the on-off-hook detection and the timing clock determines the number of impulses which have been received for a digit.

The translator is accessed at the end of every subscriber-dialed digit (from the first to the sixth) until it sees a valid routing request. Capable of being accessed up to 350 times per second, the translator operates in conjunction with the out-pulsing circuitry to provide information with a constant 640 msec interdigital period regardless of the speed of subscriber

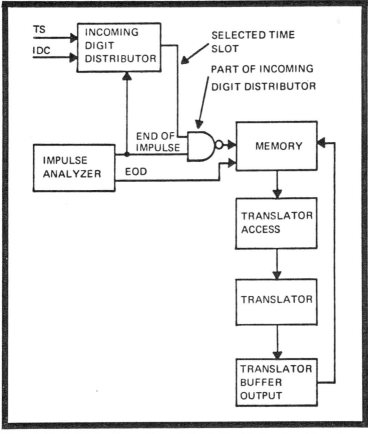

Fig. 6-9. Digit distribution and translation in the Minisender. (Stromberg-Carlson Corp.)

dialing. The two operating modes of the translator are the route-hunting mode and the automatic mode. Digit distribution and translation are diagramed in Fig. 6-9. A complete block diagram of the Minisender is shown in Fig. 6-10.

The translator uses a digit or digits of a dialed code to gain access to a route card, which is programed with routing instructions used to direct the call to its destination. All working codes are associated with such a route card. If alternate routing is provided, the code is associated with a second route card which has been programed to provide routing instructions necessary to direct the call to its destination over an alternate route. Minisenders are generally programed at the factory, but a strapping panel is available at the equipment to permit reprograming of the route cards for: (1) routing changes or rearrangements that require a change in routing instructions, (2) a change in class of service, or (3) the addition of a new route.

ROTARY SWITCHING SYSTEMS

About 10 percent of the world's local telephone lines are switched by rotary switching systems, which differ from step-by-step Strowger switches in that they do not have vertical motion as well as rotary motion. There are three distinct types of rotary switches in use, although they are applied in circuitry which does not differ basically in principle. One is the Siemens EMD uniselector, which was introduced in 1955. Another is the ITT rotary switch, a form of which was installed first as early as 1923 in Belgium. The third type is the 500-line rotary switch of L.M. Ericsson, which was also brought into service in 1923.

All rotary systems are of the progressive-type, with line-finders and selectors following in progression in a somewhat similar layout to step-by-step systems. However, they differ in two major ways: (1) the switches are power-driven, resulting generally in continuous running of the machinery in contrast with the dialed-stepping of the Strowger switches in step-by-step systems, and (2) all basic rotary systems incorporate register storage of the dialed signals and have a number of features of common control, which make them much more adaptable to modern services than has been the case with

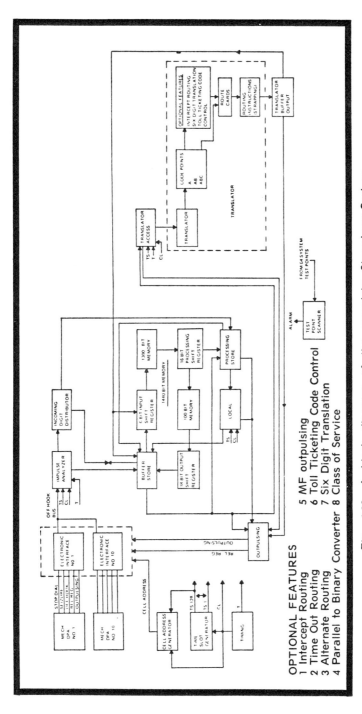

OPTIONAL FEATURES

1 Intercept Routing
2 Time Out Routing
3 Alternate Routing
4 Parallel to Binary Converter

5 MF outpulsing
6 Toll Ticketing Code Control
7 Six Digit Translation
8 Class of Service

Fig. 6-10. A block diagram of the complete Stromberg-Carlson Minisender. (Stromberg-Carlson Corp.)

121

direct control step-by-step systems. Although most rotary systems would be classed register progressive control types, some have called them full-fledged common control systems.

The EMD Rotary System

Although the EMD motorswitch can be operated directly from the pulses of the subscriber's dial, it is usually operated under indirect control. In this method the dialed pulses control a setting unit which in turn directs the switch to the required decade by means of electrical marking, which may be on an individual or a group basis. A diagram of the indirect mode of control with individual marking is shown in Fig. 5-9. Here the dial pulses operate a stepping relay in the relay set of the motorswitch. The wiper on this stepping relay marks the contact on the switch multiple, which represents the beginning of the dialed decade or the group step. The motorswitch is then started, followed by the testing by its fourth switch, the d-arm, of the marked contact on which the switch is stopped. After this decade selection, the motorswitch changes over to hunting or controlled stepping. Electrical marking of the decades eliminates the need for cam discs and cam contacts. Also, the switch remains on the last step reached during the selection and does return to a home position.

In the case of group marking, the dial pulses pass via the relay set of the switch to a common control set which serves several switches. The control set interprets the dial pulses generally by a relay circuit instead of a stepping relay. The required step in the switch multiple is marked by the control set. The control set technique, shown in Fig. 6-11, offers economic advantages so it is the preferred method for electrically marked EMD systems.

The EMD motorswitch cannot have its contact decades arranged one upon another like the levels of the Strowger switch, but only horizontally and one after another. However, the contact bank is divided into two horizontal levels arranged one upon another so that, with one full rotation of the switch, two staggered switch arms are able to reach the contacts of all outlets. The high rotation speed of the EMD motorswitch enables it to traverse a switching decade well within the duration of a dial pulse, which is about 100 msec. An ultrafast relay was developed to enable the motorswitch to stop on the required outlet despite its high rotation speed (140 to 160

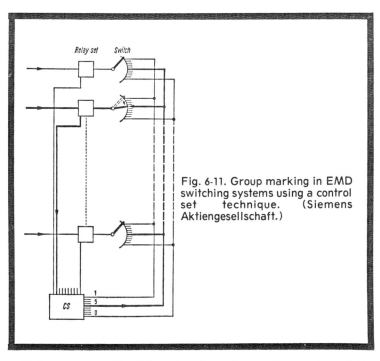

Fig. 6-11. Group marking in EMD switching systems using a control set technique. (Siemens Aktiengesellschaft.)

outlets per second). This relay, inserted in the c-wire of the switch, operates with a delay of only about 2 msec and meets all requirements. Although the EMD motorswitch may be used in various combinations of line-finders and selectors, a simplified diagram of Fig. 6-12 shows its use with a subscriber line circuit (SLC), which guards a busy subscriber line against other incoming calls.

Ericsson's AGF Rotary System

With the 500-line switch, the selector system is made up of groups of 500 subscriber lines. If the number of lines does not exceed 500, only 1 numerical switching stage is required and the trunking arrangement of the exchange is that shown in

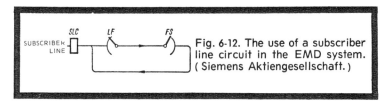

Fig. 6-12. The use of a subscriber line circuit in the EMD system. (Siemens Aktiengesellschaft.)

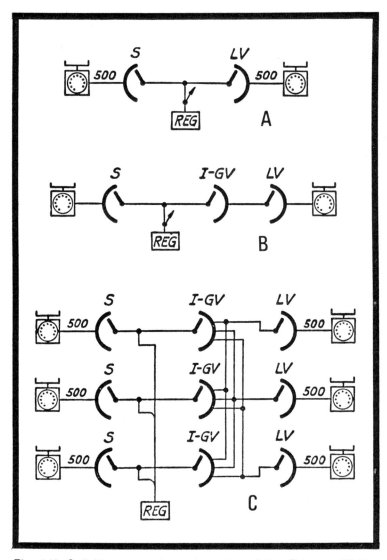

Fig. 6-13. Switching stages in various sizes of the Ericsson 500-line selector system. (L. M. Ericsson.)

Fig. 6-13A. The group contains only line-finders, registers, and final selectors. In the line-finder stage, the calling line is connected to a line-finder and a register. Thus, distribution of the traffic takes place in the final selector stage, which contains the only numerical switch. If more than 500 lines are to be connected to the exchange, an additional switching stage in the form of a group selector must be added as shown in Fig. 6-13B. As exchange requirements are expanded, the trunking arrangement is expanded in groups of 500-line capacity, as shown in Fig. 6-13C. Since the 500-line switch has both a rotary and a radial movement, the wiper arm of the group selector rotates to the multiple frame corresponding to the 500-line group of the dialed number. Then its wiper arm performs a radial movement to hunt for a free final selector in that group. By using 2 group selector stages it is possible to reduce the number of groups of switching networks to a somewhat smaller number than the ratio of the number of lines accommodated to 500. Such an arrangement is applied to exchanges which must accommodate thousands of lines.

As indicated in the above diagrams, the Ericsson 500-line selector system is register-controlled. Rather surprisingly, the registers utilize crossbar switches combined with conventional relays. The crossbar switch stores the dialed digits and the relays provide for impulse reception and control of the switching processes. In general one vertical of a crossbar switch is used for each digit. When the subscriber dials a digit and the train of impulses from the dial is complete, some of the relays in the chain will be operated. Via contacts on these relays a marking circuit is closed to one of the 10 horizontal magnets of the crossbar switch corresponding to the dialed digit. The horizontal magnet causes the horizontal bar to rotate, and immediately thereafter the vertical magnet operates in the vertical or verticals in which the digit is to be stored. The horizontal bar and relay chain are then released, after which the register is free to receive the next digit. The transfer of the digits from the relay chain to the crossbar switch occurs very rapidly. A second relay chain stores revertive impulses from the selector, which the register is to direct to the wanted position. The digit-marking circuits from the verticals of the crossbar switch, which act as translation circuits, are connected successively to this second relay chain, which has 25 different positions corresponding to the number of frames or routes in the multiple of the 500-line selector. The register also has another chain of relays, which provides supervision in the starting of the selectors and in the successive connection of the translation circuits from the crossbar switch to the revertive impulse chain for each selector setting. Thus, a register-translator function is performed.

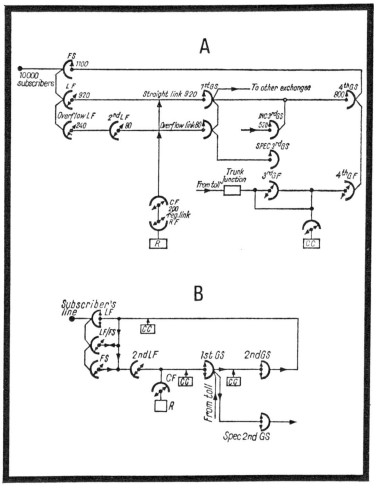

Fig. 6-14. (A) Junction diagram of a 7A rotary exchange. (B) Junction diagram of a 7DU main exchange. (ITT—International Telephone and Telegraph Corp.)

The ITT Rotary Systems

The rotary systems installed in many countries of the world are based on the original rotary system developed in this country by the Bell System in the early part of the 20th century. Although the basic system is old, it is register controlled and able to cope with the new telephone service situation far better than direct-control systems. Four systems in their 7-series have been installed by ITT as follows:

126

1. (7A) A register-control system using sliding-contact rotary switches controlled by revertive pulses, used for large exchanges.

2. (7B) Register-controlled system using single-motion switches with revertive pulsing.

3. (7D) Register controlled system using single-motion switches controlled by markers, which receive impulses forwarded from the registers. This system is used mainly for rural areas.

4. (7E) Register-controlled using single-motion switches. The use of permanent ac phase marking for the positioning of the selectors avoids impulse counting. A static line circuit is used.

In these systems the rotary switches are capable of finding only a determined arc terminal, which has to be marked by the application of a marking voltage. In the case of the linefinder, marking is effected by the subscriber's line circuit, and in the case of group selection by the circuits of the passing free lines. In the case of group selection the direction to be selected is determined by the trip spindle in the 7A system and by the marker circuit in the 7D system. The former allows only the brushes associated with the direction to be selected to contact the arc. The marker effects a second marking, which together with the marking coming from the free line determines the arc terminal where the switch is to stop. In the case of line selection, the register of the 7A system or the marker of the 7D system provides for the marking of the called subscriber.

The junction diagram of a 7A exchange, capable of handling 10,000 lines, is shown in Fig. 6-14A and the junction diagram of a 7DU main exchange is shown in Fig. 6-14B. About 50 percent of the local lines served by ITT's rotary exchanges are switched by the 7A system and about 30 percent by the 7D system.

7

Electromechanical Crossbar Systems

The introduction of a crossbar system in the U.S. occurred because of the advantages it offered over the panel system, which was widely used in the Bell System during the 1930s. The crossbar switch offered shorter call completing times, better transmission characteristics, reduced maintenance, a single appearance of each line on the frames for both originating and terminating traffic, and the ability to add PBX-hunting lines without number changes.

OLDER CROSSBAR SYSTEMS

Crossbar switching was introduced to the United States in 1938, with the advent of the No. 1 crossbar system. The No. 1 crossbar system utilizes common control with a combined concentration-expansion switching network for both originating and terminating traffic. Originating and terminating registers and markers at the originating and terminating offices, respectively, are major elements in the common-control portion of the system.

Crossbar switches made up of a 10x20 array of contacts are utilized in this system. One switch can normally be used for as many as 10 simultaneous talking paths. Frames consisting of, in general, 20 such switches each are designated: line link, district link, office link, and incoming link. The switches of each frame are interconnected so that a large number of internal paths or links interconnect any of the input circuits to any of the output circuits. Figure 7-1 shows a basic No. 1 crossbar system. Although it continues to serve millions of local lines, the No. 1 crossbar system was superseded in the 1940s by the No. 4 and No. 5 crossbar systems.

No. 4 Toll Crossbar System

The No. 4 crossbar system with provision for 4-wire operation in toll circuits was installed first in August, 1943, in

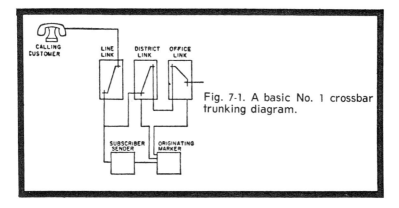

Fig. 7-1. A basic No. 1 crossbar trunking diagram.

Philadelphia. It has undergone many changes since, and has been designated as No. 4A crossbar since 1950.

One of the most significant additions to the No. 4 crossbar system is the electronic translator. When combined with the translator the system is designated 4A/ETS, as shown in Fig. 7-2. The use of an electronic translator with the No. 4A

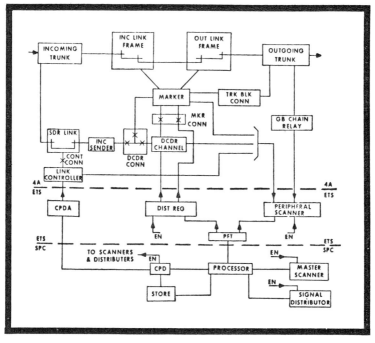

Fig. 7-2. A No. 4A crossbar exchange with the addition of an electronic translator (ETS). (IEEE—Transactions on Communication Technology.)

crossbar system is primarily intended to replace electromechanical decoders and card translators used to perform route translation functions. It provides greater flexibility of routing strategies, improved maintenance facilities, and the capacity for the introduction of new direct distance dialing service features through the use of stored-program control. With the ETS the translation speed is reduced from 150 msec to about 10 msec. Route translation changes in the standard No. 4A system require the manual replacement of cards, while with ETS they are electrically alterable via teletypewriter input. Also, with ETS major translation changes are electrically alterable via magnetic tape input. Emergency translation changes can be made from key inputs in a network management console with ETS, while manual procedures are required without it.

The code translation capacity of the No. 4A system is limited to 1,200 3-digit and 19,000 6-digit codes, while with ETS it is virtually unlimited. Normally 2 classes of service are available per office, but with ETS 16 classes of service are available per office with a capability of easily expanding beyond this number.

With regard to maintenance, trouble reporting is provided in the regular No. 4A system by punched cards which correlate the malfunction with a major unit. With ETS a teletypewriter printout correlates the malfunction with a subunit, which can be replaced by a plug-in assembly.

No. 5 Crossbar

The first installation of a No. 5 crossbar switching system was placed in service in 1948 near Philadelphia. It was a typical metropolitan fringe office of 4000 lines interconnecting with step-by-step offices and with the No. 4 toll crossbar office in Philadelphia. The internal design of the equipment was changed considerably from that of the No. 1 system. Of particular economic importance was the reduction in the number of different types of switching frames and units. A flexible switching plan was developed to permit the No. 5 system to serve relatively small central office requirements as well as larger ones economically. As a result, the No. 5 system could handle offices varying in size from less than 2,000 lines to more than 10,000 lines. As shown in Fig. 7-3, the No. 5 system has only two types of switching frames—the line link and the trunk link—compared with four types of frames—the line link, district link, office link, and incoming link—in the No. 1 system.

The line-link frame of the initial No. 5 system had half as many secondary switch outlets as that of the No. 1 system, yet it could serve as much traffic as the equivalent frame of the latter. The basic line-link frame of the No. 5 system had a capacity of 290 lines; but by the use of 100- and 200-line supplementary bays, it was possible to serve as many as 590 lines, the same as in the No. 1 system. A maximum of 40 line-link frame groups could be accommodated by a No. 5 crossbar unit in comparison with the 80 line-link capacity of a No. 1 crossbar unit. The trunk-link frame provides the means for connecting the line-link frames to all of the outgoing and incoming trunks as well as to all of the subscriber dial registers. In addition to having a capacity of 200 junctors to all of the line-link frames, this frame has 160 outlets to which trunks and registers can be connected.

THE MODERN No. 5 SYSTEM

There have been a number of improvements in the No. 5 crossbar system over the years. Some of these changes in-

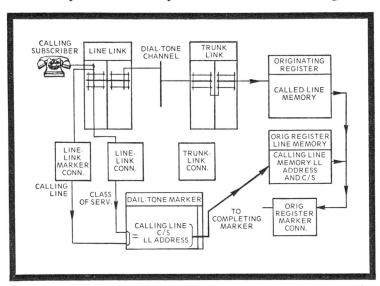

Fig. 7-3. No. 5 crossbar system showing the flow of subscriber-originated inpulsing signals.

volving the line-link and trunk-link frames are described next. Also described is the use of markers in the modern No. 5 system.

Line-Link Frame

There are two general types of line-link frames currently used in the modern No. 5 system. The newer design, which employs wire-spring relays instead of flat-spring relays for certain nonspeech-path functions, has been provided since 1955. These versions of the line-link frame are available in two sizes—190 lines and 290 lines. The 290-line frame, which is most commonly used, is a 2-bay framework with ten 200-point crossbar switches in each bay. One and one-half switches on each level are used as line switches. Each vertical on a line switch is used for a subscriber line, except one which is used for no-test access to the remaining 29. One advantage of using a vertical for each subscriber line is that the off-normal springs of the hold magnet of the crossbar switch can be used as a cutoff relay. The half switches not used as line switches are used for junctors, thus 10 verticals are provided for terminating the junctors on each level. Line links appear on the horizontals of the switches with 10 line links on each switch. These line links are distributed among the 10 junctor switches with 1 line link to 1 horizontal on each of the 10 junctor switches. This system of line links permits each line on a line link frame to reach any 1 of the 100 junctors serving that frame.

Since each common basic line switch is made up of one and one-half 200-point crossbar switches, the 290-line basic line link frame has a capacity of 300 line-switch verticals (30 to each switch) and 100 line links. However, the actual number of subscriber lines on this frame is 290 because 10 line-switch verticals (1 on each line switch) are required for no-test operation, such as obtaining access to busy lines from the local test desk and verification of busy lines. Greater line capacity is provided by the addition of supplementary bays of switches as in the initial design of the No. 5 system. Line-link frames of any size available are universal in that all classes of subscriber lines may be assigned to any frame. The No. 5 exchange can accommodate a maximum of 60 or 100 service classes if all of the markers are of the wire-spring relay type and 30 service classes if flat-spring-relay type completing or combining markers are employed. The engineering capacity of a No. 5 crossbar line-link frame is 1260 busy-hour CCS. The first step in establishing frame size for a new office is to estimate the total busy-hour CCS of the line-link frame office. Following this estimate the next step is to calculate the theoretical number of line terminations per line-link frame which will load the frames to 1260 CCS. The number of line-link frames required is determined by dividing the estimated total, working, line-link frame terminations at the end of the engineering period by the theoretical terminations required to load the frames as estimated. When the result indicates a fractional frame requirement beyond the closest whole number, a decision must be made whether to reduce or raise the number of frames to the nearest whole number.

The Trunk-Link Frame

The fundamental trunk-link frame is a 2-bay framework having ten 200-point, 3-wire crossbar switches in the junctor bay and ten 200-point, 6-wire crossbar switches in the trunk bay. The frame has capacity for terminating 200 junctors, which are used to interconnect the trunk-link frames and line-link frames. The trunk switches provide terminations for a maximum of 160 circuits. In general this frame is very similar in design to the initial one.

The Marker Group

Markers are the principal elements of common-control equipment in the No. 5 crossbar system. They are used in the completion of every call. The number of markers required in an office varies according to the size of the office and the amount of traffic to be handled. A marker group consists of a maximum of 12 markers and their associated equipment, which may serve a maximum of 40,000 numbers. In the original design of the No. 5 system only one type of marker was provided. Called the **combined marker**, it handled all marker tasks. These included dial-tone, intraoffice, outgoing, incoming, tandem, toll-computing, intermarker group, junctor, reverting, and pulse-conversion calls. Since the initial No. 5 design, the combined marker has been abandoned and gradually replaced by a more efficient separate subgroup of dial-tone and completing markers.

These separate markers were developed as part of a cost reduction program, after operating experience had shown that about 35 percent of the total combined marker usage was required by dial-tone calls and that the other 65 percent was used by the call-completing call operations. As a result, the marker group was divided into two subgroups. One consists of a maximum of four dial-tone markers and the other consists of a maximum of eight call completing markers. The purpose of the dial-tone marker in the No. 5 crossbar system is to set up connections between the calling-subscriber line and an originating register. The register then returns dial tone as a "start dialing" signal to the subscriber. This involves connections between the dial-tone marker and a line-link frame through the line-link marker connector and line-link connector, to the trunk-link frame through the trunk-link connector and to the originating register line memory frame as shown in Fig. 7-3.

Call-completing markers are associated with most of the other switching operations of the No. 5 crossbar system. The completing marker common equipment frame accommodates the functional units associated with trunk-link frame and trunk selection, identification of calling- and called-line locations on line-link frames, channel test and selection, junctor group and pattern control, ringing-switch control, sender and sender-connector selection, route advance and recycle control, sender-link control, trunk charge information on intraoffice or outgoing call, identification of trunk class on incoming call, identification of AMA recorder number for AMA charging, pulse-conversion class control, overall timing, cross detection and master-test-frame connector and trouble-recorder control. Several other frames of equipment associated with the completing marker common equipment frame are: translator and code-treatment frame, route-relay frame, code-conversion frame, supplementary-service-treatment relay frame, PBX allotter frame, foreign-area translator frame and foreign-area-translator connector frame, and a 4-wire frame provided on an optional basis when the marker group is arranged for 4-wire network traffic. Figures 7-4 through 7-6 show the connections required for establishing intraoffice connection, outgoing trunk connection, and incoming trunk connection, respectively. They are numbered to indicate the order in which the connections take place.

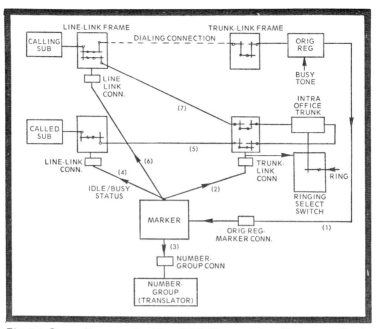

Fig. 7-4. Connections required in establishing an intraoffice connection in a No. 5 crossbar exchange.

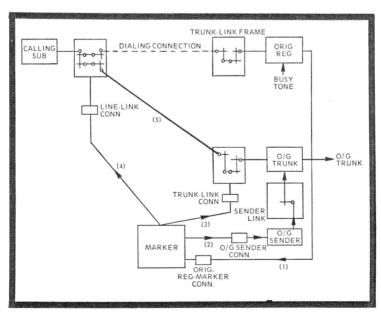

Fig. 7-5. An outgoing trunk connection in No. 5 crossbar.

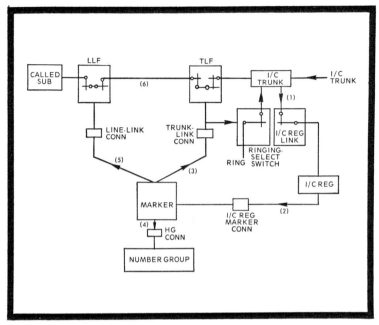

Fig. 7-6. An incoming trunk connection in No. 5 crossbar.

JAPAN'S C400 CROSSBAR SYSTEM

As shown in Fig. 7-7, the trunking scheme of the speech-path switches of the C400 is similar in general to that of No. 5 crossbar. Also, the common control is characterized by dial-tone and completing markers. However, as an overall system the C400 has a wider range of applications—from small local central offices to tandem and toll operation. With this broad range of applications, the C400, shown in Fig. 7-8, is the standard crossbar-switching system in Japan. In a small-exchange application (800 to 3000 subscribers) a combined marker is used. The main switching network is made up of four stages of switching—that is, with link frames of two stages each. A line-link frame has a 1240 HCS capacity and an accommodation for 760 subscriber lines, while a trunk-link frame can accommodate as many as 180 trunk lines. One exchange unit consists of 16 frames. Other equipment—trunks, registers, etc.—is the same as that used in larger offices. In the large system, a line-link frame has a 3100 HCS capacity and can accommodate 1920 subscriber lines, while a trunk-link frame can accommodate as many as 360 trunks. Of course, the number of frames in an exchange unit determines its overall capacity.

In its tandem application the C400 provides regular central-office switching functions as well as a tandem switching service. In this case, it is desirable that incoming trunks or outgoing trunks arranged for handling tandem traffic shall also handle traffic for completion to or origination from this office, since it is generally economical to combine these two types of traffic over the same trunk group. To permit this dual use, it is necessary to provide such outgoing or incoming trunks with both trunk-link and line-link frame locations. In the C400 type crossbar office with a tandem

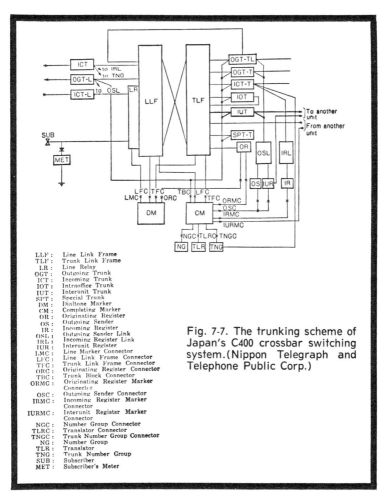

LLF :	Line Link Frame
TLF :	Trunk Link Frame
LR :	Line Relay
OGT :	Outgoing Trunk
ICT :	Incoming Trunk
IOT :	Intraoffice Trunk
IUT :	Interunit Trunk
SPT :	Special Trunk
DM :	Dialtone Marker
CM :	Completing Marker
OR :	Originating Register
OS :	Outgoing Sender
IR :	Incoming Register
OSL :	Outgoing Sender Link
IRL :	Incoming Register Link
IUR :	Interunit Register
LMC :	Line Marker Connector
LFC :	Line Link Frame Connector
TFC :	Trunk Link Frame Connector
ORC :	Originating Register Connector
TBC :	Trunk Block Connector
ORMC :	Originating Register Marker Connector
OSC :	Outgoing Sender Connector
IRMC :	Incoming Register Marker Connector
IURMC :	Interunit Register Marker Connector
NGC :	Number Group Connector
TLRC :	Translator Connector
TNGC :	Trunk Number Group Connector
NG :	Number Group
TLR :	Translator
TNG :	Trunk Number Group
SUB :	Subscriber
MET :	Subscriber's Meter

Fig. 7-7. The trunking scheme of Japan's C400 crossbar switching system.(Nippon Telegraph and Telephone Public Corp.)

Fig. 7-8. C-400 type crossbar switching system. (Nippon Telegraph and Telephone Public Corp.)

switching function, outgoing trunks are provided with both trunk-link and line-link frame locations. When the tandem traffic is less than the terminating traffic, it is economical to provide the outgoing trunks with both trunk-link and line-link locations. The trunk-link location is used when a call going out on a tandem trunk originates from this office. When the incoming call is to be switched to a connecting office through this office, the line-link frame location is used. Since there are at least two C400 crossbar units in the same installation for the sake of continuity of service, the incoming trunk serves both units as shown in Fig. 7-9. The determination of which unit shall handle the call is made by the common-control circuit of the incoming register-marker connector from the number received from the incoming register. This operation results in the connection of the incoming register and completing marker in the selected unit.

A special feature of the C400 is its 2-stage sender link, which results in the efficiency of the outgoing sender being improved to 70 percent in comparison with 45 percent in a conventional 1-stage link. Actually, the C400 system is a relatively new one, having gone into general service in 1967.

ITT'S PENTACONTA CROSSBAR SYSTEM

The Pentaconta system was developed in 1953 and the first exchange was cut over at Cento, Italy, in 1954. Its basic element is a crossbar switch with 22 verticals and 14 horizontal bars, 1 of which is used as a changeover bar to provide for switching 52 outlets. In the first design, 500-subscriber units were each served by 2 markers, but after about 4 years of field experience with several installations it was decided to change the line unit to 1000 subscribers. This design, in which 2 markers can handle 6000 calls per hour with a marker-holding time per call ranging between 450 and 500 msec, has been installed rather widely outside of the U.S. by ITT. The 1000B system is adaptable for public exchanges ranging from 1,000 to 50,000 lines.

The block diagram of a Pentaconta exchange of the 1000B type is shown in Fig. 7-10. The line- and group-selection units use 2-stage crossbar switches under the control of markers for conditional-selection operation, while the incoming and outgoing junctions use only relay groups. Figure 7-11 shows the arrangement of a line or group selection unit. The two crossbar switching stages are the primary and the secondary, or terminal stage. Each stage consists of several sections

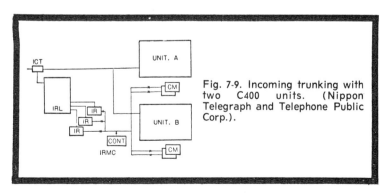

Fig. 7-9. Incoming trunking with two C400 units. (Nippon Telegraph and Telephone Public Corp.).

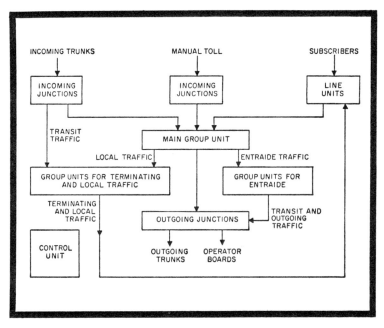

Fig. 7-10. The functions of the 1000 B Pentaconta exchange. (ITT International Telephone and Telegraph Corp.).

composed of one or more multiswitches (the name for individual crossbar switches in the Pentaconta system). The standard group-selection unit for a large exchange might include 7 primary sections, each consisting of 2 multiswitches having 22 verticals to provide 2 x 7 x 22 or 308 inlets; and 20 secondary sections, each of one multiswitch with 14 verticals. Each secondary section gives access to 52 outlets so that an incoming junction connected to an inlet of the primary stage has access to 52 x 20 or 1040 outlets. The 2-stage link arrangement is thus the equivalent of a selector with 1040 terminals.

The 52 outlets of the primary sections are divided into two classes: 40 outlets (20 x 2) are assigned to the direct junctions between primary and secondary sections, and 12 outlets are reserved for alternative routing of calls within a selection unit.

The latter is referred to as an **entraide**, meaning "mutual aid" in French. It permits the extension of path choice by allowing one primary level access to the primary-secondary cross-connecting paths of another, and provides a measure of protection against blocking.

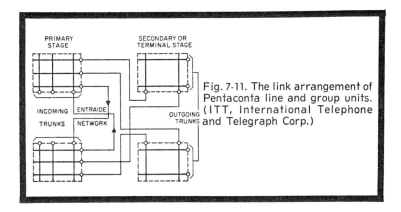

Fig. 7-11. The link arrangement of Pentaconta line and group units. (ITT, International Telephone and Telegraph Corp.)

L. M. ERICSSON'S ARF AND AKF EXCHANGES

L. M. Ericsson's ARF series of exchanges, which use crossbar switches of the basic type described in Chapter 4, are the most widely used crossbar exchanges they produce. During the past decade they have introduced another type of crossbar switch called the Code switch. Exchanges using this switch are designated as the AKF series. Although the Code switch systems have certain advantages for large and medium-sized exchange installations, they are not yet widely used, and most of the new installations are still utilizing the ARF series with the more conventional crossbar switches.

The speech-path switching stages of Ericsson crossbar exchanges are usually divided into what is called the **subscriber stage** and the **group selector stage**, each of which is served by its own marker. Thus, stage-by-stage marking is applied. In the switching network, one major difference from the Bell System crossbar techniques is found in the way in which the subscriber lines are connected to the crossbar switch. In the Ericsson systems, the subscriber lines terminate on the horizontals of the switch, while in the Bell Systems they are allotted to the crossbar verticals. The Ericsson method requires that both line and cutoff relays must be provided in external line circuits, while with the Bell System arrangement the vertical magnets of the crossbar switch can provide the cutoff relay functions. However, the Ericsson method does permit operator break-in, which is a European requirement.

8 Electronic Exchanges with Wired Logic

The possibilities of utilizing electronic components and circuitry in telephone switching systems was not given serious consideration until after World War II and no significant developmental activity was undertaken until after the invention of the transistor in the late 1940s. Since switching logic circuits can be realized with either electromechanical components in the form of relays, or electronic components in the form of diodes, transistors, or magnetic elements; it would seem natural to simply substitute electronic components for all of the electromechanical components in an exchange and thus construct electronic telephone exchanges in this fashion. Actually, a certain amount of development of this type occurred, as in the case of electronic directors and register-translators which were associated with the step-by-step and rotary system already installed. However, the mere substitution of electronic switching elements for electromechanical ones does not take advantage of the main benefits to be derived through the use of electronic techniques. In addition, it has not been found practical up to this time to use solid-state components as the speech- or data-path switching elements in local central-office exchanges, although the remainder of the exchange can be almost completely electronic.

Electronic switching offers several advantages over electromechanical switching, one of which is much higher switching speeds. The highest switching speeds would be attained by using either solid-state crosspoints or time-division switching of the speech circuits. However, neither of these approaches has proved practical for local central-office exchanges. Solid-state crosspoints suffer from their limited off-on impedance ratio, resulting in crosstalk problems. Also, there is significant attenuation when they are "on" except for very special designs. Both time-divison switching and solid-state space-division crosspoints suffer from their limited power-handling capacity, which makes them incompatible with the ringing-power requirements of installed telephone instruments. Expensive interface equipment would be required to work with existing telephone instruments. The economic barrier posed by this limitation alone was such that the use of true electronic switching with telephones now in the hands of subscribers was not feasible and only metallic crosspoints were considered for local central-office switching. The Bell System concluded that the crosspoints need to operate only fast enough to be compatible with the speed of the electronic common-control equipment in the exchange, and they settled for reed relays in the speech circuits.

The fact that relays were used in the speech-switching circuits of these exchanges, which incorporated electronic common equipment, led to the use of qualifying names for them. Two such names were **quasielectronic** and **semielectronic**. The Bell System referred to their central-office exchanges, No. 1 ESS and No. 2 ESS, as electronic exchanges despite their use of reed relays, and in general it became acceptable in communication circles around the world to drop the qualifying terms and to simply refer to all exchanges using electronic common control equipment as electronic exchanges, regardless of the type of switching elements used in the speech circuits.

CROSSBAR SYSTEM WITH ELECTRONICS IN CONTROL CIRCUITRY

The block diagram of a typical crossbar exchange, whether controlled by electromechanical or electronic components, is shown in Fig. 8-1. It is quite practical to design a high electronic content into the control elements of such an exchange. Integrated circuits may be used extensively in the main control with discrete components in the peripheral areas. If plug-in miniature crossbar switches are also used, a compactness compatible with the electronic componentry can be realized. Printed-circuit control cards and rack interconnection arrangements allow for an electronically controlled exchange to be expanded easily. A 2-stage system of this type might handle 500 lines, but a 4-stage system could handle up to 10,000 or 12,000 lines. In general, register and marker control in such a system would behave very much as in an electromechanically controlled exchange, but switching

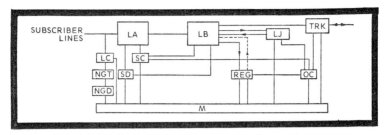

Fig. 8-1. Block diagram of a typical crossbar exchange.

speeds would definitely be faster. The miniaturized electromechanical components would be the limiting elements in the overall speed of the exchange.

In addition to the smaller physical volume of a modular design, there is the matter of ease of installation and maintenance. The integrated circuits, discrete components, and miniature relays may be soldered to printed cards, which are mounted in subracks. Connections are then made by plug and connector arrangements. Defective assemblies may be replaced readily in the case of failure of any of the components. Also, the modular arrangement allows flexibility in the exact configuration of racks and subracks used in the installation.

Although this design offers some advantages through the use of electronic componentry, it does not incorporate some of the prinicpal elements of a more sophisticated electronic exchange. It does not incorporate a full-fledged memory section and it has **wired logic**, although modules of the logic can be changed more readily through plugs and connectors than comparable electromechanical components.

Wired logic is not as disadvantageous as it might appear at first sight. If the exchange incorporates a computer-type memory, it may be designed so that such a memory is programmable without the necessity of interchanging large amounts of hardware when new programs are required. Such a design may be far more economical for a particular size of exchange than one incorporating software features for changing the program stored in the memory.

CROSSBAR SYSTEMS WITH ELECTRONIC MEMORY ONLY

Although conventional electromechanical crossbar systems can provide most of the new subscriber services, complications arise in the amount of associated equipment and devices that must be added to such exchanges to achieve such results. The key element to the provision of such services without undue complications is an electronic computer-type memory. Obviously, the programs stored in such a memory can be in the form of wired logic, or the memory might incorporate electronically alterable storage components, which could be reprogramed through external software. Either way, the electronic memory offers a more flexible arrangement for adding the new subscriber services. If it can be programed through software, it allows changes or addition to service features without any changes in hardware. If it is a wired-logic type, some flexibility can still be realized by making the memory programable through interchangeable units, or by rethreading wires through cores so that major hardware changes need not be made.

If one tried to add electronic memory to an electromechanical crossbar exchange, and there may be a real basis for such a modification due to the large number of existing crossbar exchanges with decades of service life ahead of them, the following factors would be significant.

1. A memory system capable of being reprogramed through software (so-called stored program control) requires extensive alterations in the control and trunking system of the existing exchange.

2. The wired logic approach is more economical.

3. The prospective future demands for subscriber service features are not extensive enough to make a software-controlled memory system essential.

4. It appears that a satisfactory degree of flexibility can be realized with a wired-logic control system.

The introduction of a wired-logic electronic memory into a conventional crossbar exchange would permit the following functions to be performed:

1. Translating a subscriber number into information of subscriber line location in the line-link frame or into subscriber class.

2. Translating an office code into the associated outgoing-route information.

3. Functions that permit information of subscriber line location in the line-link frame to be translated into information of the corresponding video-line location in the video-link frame or of the location terminated in the call-waiting switch.

4. Functions that permit a subscriber line location in the line-link frame to be translated into the subscriber directory number.

5. Functions that permit an abbreviated dial number to be translated into an ordinary directory number.

6. Memorizing of information that varies with time and providing such information to the common-control equipment, as required in memorizing the correspondence between subscribers and the associated trunks and memorizing the subscriber line status.

7. Memorizing various kinds of information inherent to the office or the subscribers, such as subscriber class information.

8. Memorizing information stored in each individual equipment such as trunks, registers, and senders.

In conventional crossbar exchanges, registers or senders are employed to store subscriber numbers and information of subscriber line location in the line-link frame, and some of the trunks store subscriber class information. The memory function referred to here is that of centralizing into a memory the above information.

A memory system can be introduced into an existing conventional crossbar system to perform the functions 1 to 7 above by connecting it to the markers as shown in Fig. 8-2. However, considerable rearrangement of the electromechanical circuitry would be necessary to introduce function 8 unless the memory system was designed into the exchange initially. Actually, two memories could be used to reduce the waiting time for the memory-equipment start of the marker. A ferrite-core memory of 300,000 bits could be used for an exchange with 1,500 subscribers and 500 trunks, and could provide the following service classes in addition to its number group and translator functions: (1) automatic call back (2) call forwarding (3) call waiting (3) call holding or add-on (3-way conference) (4) recorder message (5) dial transfer (Centrex) and (6) video-phone as well as subscriber control of customer services, allowing the control of such services as call forwarding and recorded message by dialing a special number from another telephone.

ELECTRONIC COMMON CONTROL

The substitution of electronic components for electromechanical ones or the attachment of electronic computer-type memories to conventional crossbar exchanges can offer considerable advantages, but they do not provide full electronic common control. It is in the full use of electronics in the control of exchanges that the most revolutionary possibilities exist. Here, as mentioned above, it is possible to store a control program in fast-operating, high-density digital memories, which can be changed readily as computer soft-

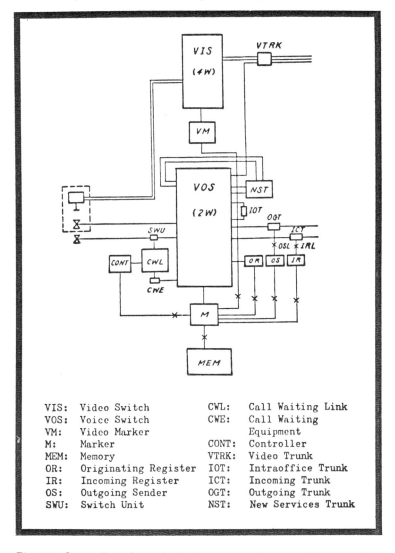

VIS:	Video Switch	CWL:	Call Waiting Link
VOS:	Voice Switch	CWE:	Call Waiting
VM:	Video Marker		Equipment
M:	Marker	CONT:	Controller
MEM:	Memory	VTRK:	Video Trunk
OR:	Originating Register	IOT:	Intraoffice Trunk
IR:	Incoming Register	ICT:	Incoming Trunk
OS:	Outgoing Sender	OGT:	Outgoing Trunk
SWU:	Switch Unit	NST:	New Services Trunk

Fig. 8-2. Connection of an electronic memory to an existing crossbar exchange. (Nippon Telegraph and Telephone Public Corp.)

ware. Thus, the need to modify hardware to provide new services is eliminated.

Stored-Program Control Exchanges

Such **stored-program control** (SPC) exchanges, as they are referred to, utilizing software techniques to the fullest extent, can be installed and programed to serve a given area without concern that later expansion in that area will require additional hardware, as long as the expansion is within the upper limit of the line capacity of the exchange. In the past, in electromechanical exchanges, it was necessary to install large sections of new hardware to accommodate expansion. With electronic exchanges, it is only necessary to reprogram the software and introduce the new program into the exchange to accommodate the expansion. It is also possible to reprogram in the same way for new types of service to the existing subscribers even when expansion in terms of the number of subscribers is not involved.

With such advantages it would appear that SPC exchanges would soon replace all existing exchanges. However, there is a matter of cost. Existing installations of electromechanical equipment cannot be replaced before a certain period of service unless an expensive sacrifice is to be made and, furthermore, the cost of SPC exchanges is such that they are not competitive for central offices serving less than a few thousand lines. In view of these economics, various versions of electronic exchanges without the readily changeable software features have been developed especially to accommodate situations involving a smaller number of lines.

Due to the heavy emphasis placed upon a technique of stored-program control by the Bell System, the use of the term has become practically synonymous with the term **electronic switching**. Actually, in a broader sense stored-program control can refer to the use of high-density memories to store the programs required for controlling the switching network of an exchange either in a **software** or **hardware** form. In the hardware form it is referred to as wired-program control (WPC), while in the software form it is referred to as stored-program control. Both are forms of stored-program control. However, the term "stored-program control" has been established through usage by its advocates to refer only to softwired programs.

Hard-wired Programable Exchanges

For the smaller exchanges the most economical approach is to use a hard-wired program. Of course, if such logic could only be changed by rewiring operations comparable in scope to those required for electromechanical exchanges, it would appear to offer little advantage. This consideration has led to the development of a type of electronic exchange intermediate between that with fully wired logic and that with fully software-stored logic. Such exchanges are referred to as programable systems. Since software-stored logic dominates the design of large electronic exchanges and since its features are so extensive, the elements of stored-program control (the term now most widely used to describe software-programed systems) are covered in a following chapter. The remainder of this chapter is devoted to the smaller electronic exchanges, which are all programable to a degree. In programable exchanges, it is possible to change the sequence of events in the common-control section by the rethreading of wires through ferrite cores in the memory system, by a revised strapping of connections, or by replacing units in the memory. The most widely used method in programable electronic exchanges involves the rerouting of wire through cores or the removal or addition of wires which pass through cores. Memory systems in which such revisions can be practiced are usually the Dimond-ring-core type.

Typical examples of hardwired programable electronic exchanges and their line capacities are the British TXE-2 (200-2,000), the ITT Metaconta 11B (100-2,000), the Automatic Electric C-1 EAX (400-2,500), the Siemens 10,000E (300-10,000), and the Automatic Electric No. 1 Crosspoint Tandem exchange (6,000).

It should be noted that all of the above systems, except the TXE-4 and the No. 1 Crosspoint Tandem, are capable of operating economically in exchange installations with comparatively small numbers of lines. However, they are extendable to overlap the lower limit of softwired SPC ex , changes, which ranges from 1000 to 2000 lines.

A REED-RELAY EXCHANGE WITH REGISTER CONTROL

The British TXE-2 exchange is manufactured by more than one company in England. The one manufactured by the Plessey Company, Ltd., under the name PENTEX is

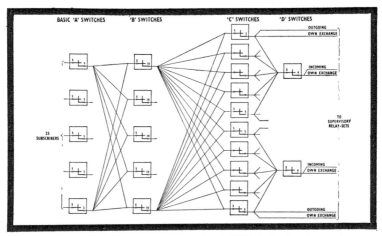

Fig. 8-3. Basic trunking arrangements of TXE-2 electronic exchange. (The Plessey Company, Ltd.)

described here. It is a register-controlled, multilink, space-division system, providing a discrete physical path for each established speech-path connection. Calls through the switching network are directed for all lines by one centralized control consisting of magnetic cores, semiconductors, and reed relays. The central-control equipment processes calls on a one-at-a-time basis but, because of electronic speeds, it can handle calls in this sequential manner without appreciable delay, even on effectively simultaneous calls. If the primary route is assumed to be an outgoing junction and the dialed information indicates a local call, the register discriminates during an interdigital pause and the original connection is released to be reestablished to an own-exchange supervisory relay set. Discrimination and rerouting similarly occur when the initial route is to an own-exchange supervisory relay set and the subscriber requires an outgoing-junction call. Originating calls are switched via a 3-stage (A, B, C) network. (See Fig. 8-3.) The same three stages are used for incoming and own-exchange terminating calls, in association with a fourth switching stage, D. When tandem switching is required, an additional path is provided, as illustrated, from the incoming route to the A-switching stage.

Each stage of switching except D is made up of multiples of a basic switch which consists of 25 reed relays in a square 5x5 array. The D switch has a 5x4 array. Each relay assembly has four reed-contact units—two of which are used for switching the speech path, the third for switching the private wire, and the fourth for switching the operate and hold circuits.

Basic Trunking Plan

The basic switch at the A stage will allow five subscribers to share five links to the next switching stage, B. These five A-B links are taken to one of each of five 5-inlet B switches. The column of 5 basic A switches shown in Fig. 8-3 will allow 25 subscribers to have access to the 5 B switches. Additional columns of basic A switches are interconnected with the first column in such a way that no two switches share more than one A-B link. This arrangement results in a good traffic-handling capability and permits a mixture of high- and low-calling-rate subscribers to be allocated at random to a group of A switches. The maximum number of basic A-switch columns which can be connected depends upon the traffic-carrying capacity of the 25 A-B links. Each B switch has 10 outlets serving 10 C switches. The B switch size is therefore 5x10. For terminating traffic, the 5x4 D switch allows four own-exchange or incoming junction supervisory relay sets to share five links to five C switches.

The trunking plan for the TXE-2 demonstrates some interesting points about a small exchange system.

1. The subscribers are low-traffic sources and traffic concentration is needed between them and supervisory circuits or registers, which are relatively expensive. Typical supervisory or register occupancy of about 0.6 erlang or more is the aim. Concentration via two switching stages is possible, but three are preferable in order to keep the A stages small for economy. A fourth stage is possible, but the extra cost and complication are usually not worthwhile.

2. Incoming circuits are high-traffic sources and can be connected directly to supervisory circuits.

3. Terminating calls from own-exchange and incoming supervisory circuits pass over four stages to subscribers' lines. The three stages C, B, and A perform in reverse the function of the A, B, and C stages for originating calls; but the D switch is added to improve access to the C switches from the incoming and own-exchange supervisory circuits and thereby reduce traffic blocking.

4. Access to registers is given from the supervisory circuits and requires the provision of a register-access switch.

Since registers are costly, they are connected to a point where traffic is high. Even so, register traffic from each supervisory circuit is less than 0.1 erlang and concentration is needed before connection to the registers. As register costs rise more crosspoints can be used for the register-access switch to improve the register load. Typical limited-function registers seldom justify more than a single stage of access—especially since both register and supervisory costs can be reduced by using more wires between registers and their access circuits. However, access-switch costs are increased.

5. Own-exchange calls are treated as half outgoing and half incoming calls to simplify the control system. The plan is in fact folded back on itself so that the same A switches, B switches, and C switches carry traffic both outgoing from, and incoming to, the subscribers.

6. Security of the switching network depends upon the availability of alternative paths via the network, and relies upon the control system to steer calls meeting trouble via switches not showing faulty behavior.

Exchange Operation

For convenience of this description it is assumed that the majority of the calls are outgoing from the electronic exchange. All originating calls therefore are initially routed via out-going supervisory relay sets. The control of path selection and the setup procedure require that the directory number of both the calling and the called subscriber be stored in a register. A first step towards this end is the generation of the caller's directory number by the calling-number generator, where EN to DN translation takes place through a Dimond ring store. This store is composed of an array of metal-tape transformer cores arranged in four rows of 10, each row representing a digit (0-9) of the subscriber's number. A wire from the subscriber's line circuit is threaded through the appropriate cores defining the subscriber's directory number. When the subscriber lifts his handset, a current pulse is produced in his line circuit and fed along the wire through the cores, resulting in the generation of an induced pulse in the secondary winding of each core threaded. The resulting pulse pattern is written into a queuing store and subsequently passed to a free register on instructions from the store control.

The process of selecting a register, connecting it to and releasing it from the queuing store takes approximately 10 msec. The queuing store will discriminate between pulse patterns arriving not less than 200 msec apart. The probability of two subscribers calling the exchange within 200 usec is on the order of 1 in 5000, and there is the same probability of a third calling pulse within 10 msec for exchanges with 180-erlang traffic.

Figure 8-4 shows a simplified diagram of the calling-number generator, queuing store, and the registers, as well as the method of EN to DN translation with a Dimond ring store. It should be noted that when a subscriber's directory number requires alteration, the corresponding output from the calling-number generator can be easily changed by a simple rethreading of a wire through the metal tape cores. This feature illustrates the programable character of the TXE-2 system.

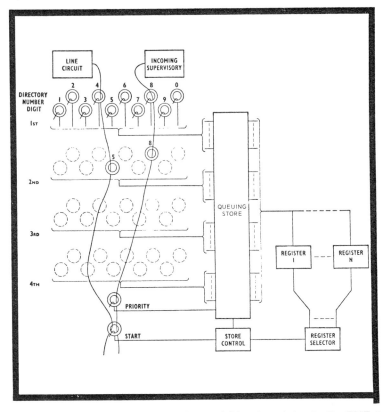

Fig. 8-4. Wires through cores of Dimond Ring translator in the TXE-2 make it programable. (The Plessey Company, Ltd.)

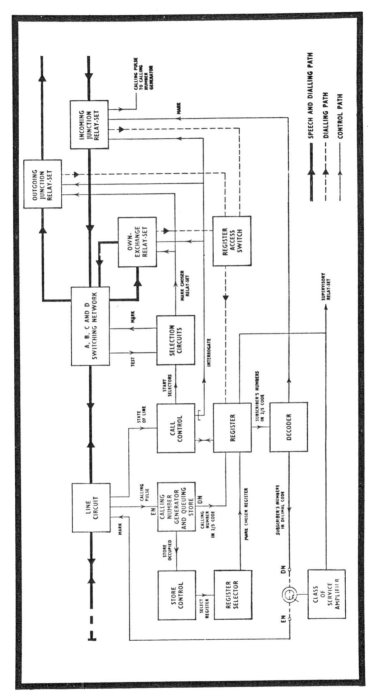

Fig. 8-5. General control diagram of the TXE-2. (The Plessey Company, Ltd.)

Originating a Call

A general control diagram of the TXE-2 exchange is shown in Fig. 8-5. It should be referred to in connection with the following description of calling techniques.

In order for a path to be set up from the subscriber's line circuit to a supervisory relay set, the register (now containing the calling subscriber's number) must have exclusive access to the call-control circuit. This is provided by a register-finder arrangement which deals with register demands one at a time—connecting simultaneously demanding registers in an arbitrarily predetermined sequence.

After connection to call control, the register passes the subscriber's pulse-generated number to the decoder where it is transformed from two-out-of-five code to decimal code and appears on a specific output lead. This lead runs through a metal-tape class-of-service core in the translation field to the line circuit's marker relay. The class-of-service core generates the subscriber's class of service (ordinary, two-part, barred, etc.) for direct acceptance by the register and supervisory relay set (when seized). The translation field enables any line circuit, irrespective of its position in the line-circuit racks, to be allocated to a particular directory number. Here again it should be noted that the TXE-2 is programable in that the changing of the class of service of a subscriber is achieved by the rethreading of the subscriber's wire through the class-of-service field.

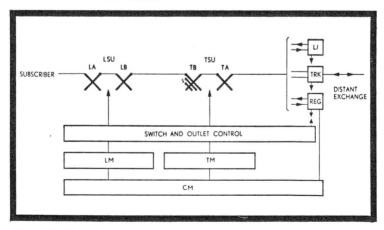

Fig. 8-6. The 4-stage version of the Metaconta 11B with hard-wired common control.

At this stage, the setting-up of the speech path is initiated by the operation of the marker relay which marks the five crosspoints of the A switch connected to the subscriber. Call control requests all free supervisory relay sets (outgoing-junction type in this case) to extend a **free mark**, so enabling a suitable C switch to be chosen. Subsequently, the selectors choose a speech path through the A, B, and C crosspoint switches, select one of the free supervisory relay-sets offered, and initiate the connection of the relay-set to the register via the register-access switch.

End-to-end marking is now imposed between the A, B, and C stages, which operate sequentially, starting at the C stage. With switching now complete between the supervisory relay set and the caller's line, a change of potential occurs at the line circuit. This change is detected by call control, resulting in the release of the call-path selection circuits and call control, and the transmission of dial tone to the subscriber's line by the register. The sequence of operations from the point of handset pickup to the receipt of dial tone takes approximately 55 msec.

ITT'S METACONTA 11B

The name Metaconta, which is an ITT trademark, is applied to soft-wired stored-program exchanges as well as hard-wired types. The 11B is a hard-wired program-controlled switching system for small and medium-size exchange applications. Using common-control-link switching, it is offered in a 2-stage version that handles 16 to 512 subscribers and in a 4-stage version that handles up to 6000. In the common control of the 2-stage version, a single marker is used for all such functions, while in the 4-stage version, separate line and trunk markers function under the control of a central marker with an associated clock generator. As shown in Fig. 8-6, the 4-stage version has two switching units—line-switching unit LSU and a trunk-switching unit TSU, each of which has primary and secondary stages. The LSU handles 256 lines with heavy traffic or 512 lines with light traffic. Up to 24 LSUs may be used in an exchange to provide for a maximum of 12,228 subscribers. The TSUs are built up accordingly.

The selection of 256-line capacities in the LSU is based on the use of the ITT Miniswitch, already described. It has 512 single-crosspoint contacts which operate in pairs. The resulting 256 pairs are arranged in a 16x16 square form.

The number-class translator consists of ferrite cores so arranged that a directory number, and originating class of service (COS) and a terminating COS are obtainable for every subscriber. The cores and their associated driving circuits are mounted on the same unit—each unit catering to 64 subscribers and giving each subscriber a 4-digit number, 1 out of 32 originating classes of service and 1 out of 16 terminating classes. Upon receipt of instructions from the line marker, the scanner and the associated drivers find the equipment or directory number of the calling or called line and the appropriate class of service information.

All units, including the Miniswitches, are in plug-in form to provide for ease of maintenance. (See Fig. 8-7.)

AUTOMATIC ELECTRIC C-1 EAX

The C-1 EAX (Fig. 8-8) employs a 3-stage switching network to serve a maximum of 2500 lines. Automatic Electric

Fig. 8-7. A plug-in printed-circuit card with integrated circuits, used in the Metaconta 11B exchange.

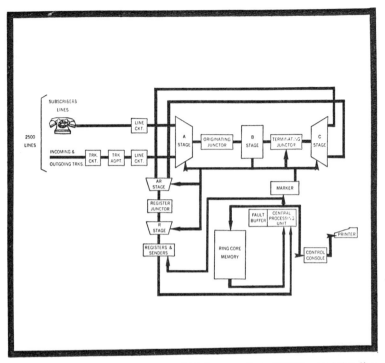

Fig. 8-8. In the GE JA chassis, a 22V 1W zener diode (Y404) regulates the sweep board supply.

crosspoint switches are arranged so that the A stage comprises a maximum of 25 matrices, each of which has 100 inlets and a maximum of 12 outlets; the B stage consists of 12 matrices, each of which has a maximum of 25 inlets and 25 outlets; and the C stage contains the same switches as the A stage. The A stage concentrates the lines to the B stage, which serves as a distribution stage to the expansion C stage. The EAX employs a central processor, which supplies coded instructions to an electronic marker circuit. The marker decodes these instructions and applies potentials to the desired crosspoint switches to establish connections.

The central processor is associated with a ring-core memory utilizing the Dimond principle. This memory contains the following numerical information: (1) the status of every line, originating junctor, register junctor, terminating junctor and register, (2) the class-of-service of these devices, (3) directory-number (DN) to equipment number (EN) translations, (4) tables of trunk-hunting groups, abbreviated-dialing codes, etc., and (5) the program which sequences the operations of the central processing unit.

The ring-core memory makes possible the programable features of this exchange. A schematic diagram shown in Fig. 8-9 illustrates the principle of the memory's operation. This memory consists of relatively large ferrite cores, through which and around which a large number of wires (called **word wires**) pass. Each core is equipped with a **sense winding**, whose output is amplified as required. If a wire passing through a core is fed with an electrical pulse, this pulse will be induced in the sense winding. A wire passing outside the core, when pulsed, will not induce a pulse in its sense winding. Thus, a word of information may be stored by pulsing wires passing through the cores. A pulse through a wire passing through a core will generate a binary 1, while a pulse through a wire outside a core will generate a binary 0. A relatively large amount of information may be stored in this type of memory

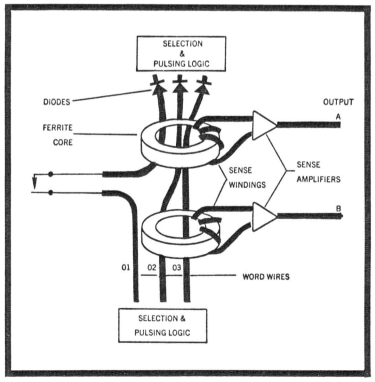

Fig. 8-9. The C-1 EAX ring-core memory system which makes it programable. (GTE Automatic Electric Labs, Inc.)

by the use of many wires. Any word of it is accessible at any time by pulsing the appropriate wire.

The ring-core memory is mounted on a number of modules, each of which contains 20 cores, 720 word wires, 2 terminal arrays, and 36 diode cards. With this method of construction it is easy to remove, add, or change a word wire. For example, when a subscriber moves and changes his line and wishes to keep the same directory number, it is necessary to change a word wire.

The Siemens ESK 10,000E

This exchange is another programable one. Its subscriber- and route-switching networks are composed of ESK relays. An ESK relay is a small crosspoint unit with palladium-silver contacts. It is used not only as a local exchange, but as a transit exchange as well. Either 2-stage or 4-stage trunking units are available depending upon the application.

The common-control equipment, although hard-wired, follows computer principles. Transistor-transistor logic is employed in this equipment, which performs its functions in accordance with a stored program. Markers connect inlets to outlets. Programing is effected in the microprogram area by inserting wires in the read-only memories with transformer cores. The programs are 2 x 1024 words at 12 bits per device with a cycle time of 1 usec. An instruction word comprising 12 bits is made up as follows: 6 bits for the address of the switching point, 5 for 1 of 27 instructions, and 1 for parity check. All information is processed serially, character by character. The character format is six bits to take the two-out-of-six register input into account. The stores in the translators are easily changed, read-only memories with fairly large transformer cores. They handle 100 words at 48 bits per plug-in storage shelf with a cycle time of 3 usec. These stores are used for translation processes which may vary during the operation of the exchange—code, trunk group, etc.

Automatic Electric No. 1 Crosspoint Tandem

This exchange, which is an excellent example of the programable type, uses a 4-stage switching network with reed-relay crosspoints (called Correeds by AE). The common control is in wired logic, distributed among a number of subsystems and implemented as follows:

1. Register-senders—electromechanical
2. Register-sender access network—electromechanical
3. Register-sender access control—electronic
4. Assigners—electronic
5. Translator memory—nondestructive, mechanically alterable
6. Markers—electronic

Although the No. 1 XPT exchange is hard-wired, considerable flexibility is provided in programing with regard to trunk-class information, address-translation information, and so forth. In these instances the information is stored in the translator's nondestructive-readout memory, which is programable through diode-pinboard matrices.

These pinboards, which are the main element of the translator, are mounted on logic-size cards in configurations of 3, 6, and 10 pinboards to a card. Three types of pins are used. One is a shorting type with a white handle, and the other two are diode-type pins with red or blue handles, depending upon the polarity of the diode. Several functional logic cards have been developed specifically for this translator as follows: (1) converter from two-out-of-five to decimal, with parity checking, (2) group-select card, (3) major-group-selection card, (4) code and class combination card, and (5) subgroup-selection card.

The hardware programing of the translator involves the physical insertion of pins into the various pinboards. In the class encoder, each 50x40 pinboard card corresponds to 100 inlet locations or incoming trunks. For each inlet location there is pinned a 3-digit class mark in two-out-of-five code. In the code and class-selection circuit there is pinned, in decimal format, every combination of codes and class marks needed to generate the desired number of outgoing trunk groups.

9   *The Elements of Stored-Program Control*

The term **stored-program control** may be a misnomer, but it is now almost universally accepted to describe a type of electronic switching control in which the controlling programs are stored in software which can be readily changed, or at least changed somewhat faster than hardware. The idea of stored programs in telephone switching is not new. For instance, in electromechanical crossbar systems, memory may be considered to reside in the registers and senders, and logic in the markers. The memory knows which telephones to connect and the logic decides the paths to be taken between them. Thus, it is seen even before the computer age telephone switching systems embodied the elements of computer control. However, it was not until much computer development had evolved that the full potential of stored-program control with software programs could manifest itself.

Although the complexity of most stored-program exchanges would lead one to believe otherwise, it must be recognized that stored-program computer control can be added to any electromechanical exchange having a marker system in its common-control section. It is only necessary to monitor the state of some relays in the marker, transmission relay sets and in the calling-line identification relays. As the marker operates on a calling line the identification of that line, transmission register, and allocated register may be stored in the computer. The dialed-in digits stored in the register may also be monitored and fed to the computer. Then under computer control, the normal transfer of the stored sub-scriber-identification digits from the register to a highway must be replaced by a computer-generated number which depends not only upon the dialed code, but the identity of the calling subscriber and the state of the class of service store of the calling and called parties. In such a role the computer acts as a sophisticated register-translator, which can provide a

162

high proportion of the services normally associated with the stored-program control of complex SPC exchanges. Such a system, shown in Fig. 9-1, has undergone considerable development at the University of Essex in England and has been referred to as the **Essex System of Add-on SPC** by its developers.

The block diagram of Fig. 9-2 represents an integrated SPC exchange. The **central control** is fed by three elements: a scanner, a call store, and a program store. The central control feeds to the switching network and a signal distributor, which in turn feeds to a trunking section. Since we are to deal with the elements of stored-program control in this chapter, we will discuss here only briefly the role of the scanner and the signal distributor and treat them more fully later. Suffice it to say that every telephone system embodies some mechanism for detecting service requests and supervising calls in progress. Input information of this nature is furnished in typical SPC exchanges by the scanning or sampling of lines, trunks, and various diagnostic points at discrete intervals of time as directed by the system. In addition to the scanning function there must be means provided to operate and release relays in trunk, service, and power-control circuits. The signal distributors translate orders received from the central control and distribute high-power, long-duration pulses to various relays in typical SPC exchanges. Also, switching networks in SPC exchanges may range from reed-relay arrays and crossbar coordinates to solid-state arrays, and are not specifically related to the SPC function.

TYPICAL STORED-PROGRAM EXCHANGE

It is in the **central processor**, the **call store**, and the **program store** that the key elements of the stored program system really lie. Sometimes the call store is referred to the **process store** and the program store is referred to as the **instruction and translation store** to better describe their functions. This is the case in an experimental stored-program-switching system developed by Automatic Electric to test stored-program techniques and develop practical means for applying these techniques. Although this exchange was not produced and installed in any quantity, its elements illustrate very well those of a stored program system and have been

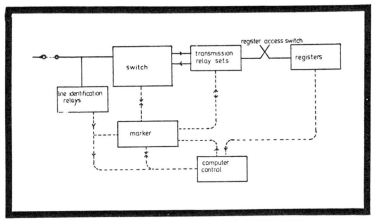

Fig. 9-1. The essex system of add-on SPC (IEEE-ISS Record).

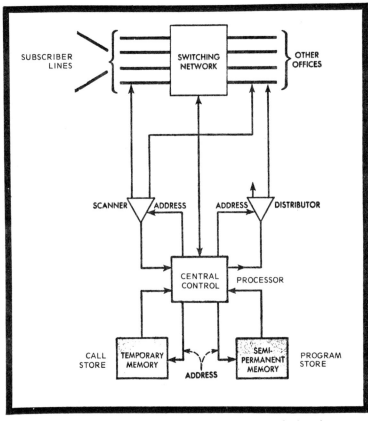

Fig. 9-2. The basic elements of a stored-program control exchange.

164

chosen for our purposes of describing typical units of an SPC system. The common-control portion of this system is straightforward in design and can be presented in some detail to illustrate the operation of an SPC system without going into many distracting side effects. It consists of a central processor, an instruction and translation (program) store, and a process (call store), as shown in Fig. 9-3. This system was designed to handle a maximum of 10,000 lines and trunks in a central-office application.

The Central Processor

In this system the central processor is a specialized digital computer, which continuously executes instructions—at the rate of some 180,000 per second—of a program stored in the instruction and translation (program) store. Every 5.5 usec, the program places an address on bus B6, receives the instruction stored at this address via B7, and executes the instruction. Thus, the stored program governs the entire behavior of the central office.

A number of flip-flop storage registers and a number of logic circuits execute the various instructions inside the

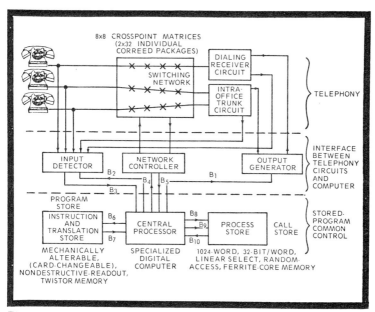

Fig. 9-3. An exchange which demonstrates all the basic features of stored-program-control operation (GTE Automatic Electric Labs, Inc.).

central processor, which has a repertoire of some 45 different instructions. These may be grouped into three categories: (1) instructions that manipulate the contents of the internal storage registers, (2) instructions transmitting commands to and receiving responses from other units, and (3) instructions to make decisions.

Decision instructions differ from nondecision instructions in that when executing a decision instruction, the central processor makes a test and chooses the next instruction from one of two places in the program store, depending upon the outcome of the test. After executing a nondecision instruction, the central processor has no choice as to what instruction is to be executed next.

The logic system in the central processor uses conventional diode-transistor-logic (DTL) NAND gates. In construction it is an interconnected group of standard printed-wiring-card types, capable of communicating with the other subsystems via cable drivers and receivers. In terms of active components it consists of approximately 6,000 transistors and 25,000 diodes, and is implemented with 385 printed wiring cards. These cards are housed in files mounted in groups of 12 in 7-foot-tall racks. In the central processor 10 card files are used for electronic circuitry and 2 card files for power. Thus, one 7-inch rack houses the central processor. The printed wiring cards plug into 46-pin connectors, which are wired together using wire-wrap techniques.

The Program Store

The **program, or instruction and translation store** is a mechanically alterable (card-changeable), nondestructive readout, twistor memory. This store is a 20,480-word, 32-bit-per-word system. Here the information is stored by punching holes in copper code sheets, which are inserted into the memory modules. The **twistor element** is used to sense the presence or absence of copper in the immediate vicinity of the bit location. The memory is organized as 10,240 double-length words of 64 bits each. There are 10,240 tape-wound switch cores, and each core is assigned to select a double-length word. These switch cores are organized in a biased switch-core matrix, called a primary matrix, the cores of which are selected by four secondary matrixes using the same type of core.

The program store communicates with the central processor on a private bus system. Since the memory is a **read-only** type, its contents cannot be altered by the central processor. A program instruction is brought to the central processor when it flashes the address of a desired location on bus B6. The store replies in about 2 usec by placing the contents of this location on bus B7. Thus, the buses B6 and B7 are the most heavily used buses in the entire system. The 16 address bits are decoded to select the proper cores in the secondary matrixes, which in turn activate circuits to select the proper core in the primary matrix. The output of the core in the primary matrix addresses its double-length word. One of the address bits is used to select which of the 2 groups of 32 bits making up the double-length word that is to be placed in the 32-bit data register.

Not all store locations contain instructions. In addition, a part of the program store is used for translation tables. The conventional translations from directory numbers to the terminal appearance of subscriber lines as well as translation tables containing class-of-service information and abbreviated dialing lists of individual subscribers are included. In general, translation tables would include all of the necessary information to implement any new service features to be offered by the system.

The code sheets for the memory of the program store are produced on an electromechanical punch capable of X-Y (horizontal and vertical) movement. Each of the 16 punches is used to selectively punch an 8x8 array of bits. Circuitry for the control and selection of punches is controlled by coded IBM cards which are read on an IBM card reader.

The Process (Call) Store

The **call store** is a 1024-word, 32-bit-per-word, linear select, random-access, ferrite-core memory capable of operating in two modes: read-restore and clear-write. The cycle time of this memory in either mode of operation is 5.5 usec and the access time to any word is 2 usec. The 32-bit locations in this store are addressed by the central processor via bus B8. In contrast with the program store, the contents of the call store can be changed by the central processor.

A call-store cycle begins with a command from the central processor. Upon recognizing this command, the call store decodes the first 10 bits of the 16-bit address generated by the central processor to select the driver and switch combination for the desired word. If the central processor requests a read-restore operation, the driver-switch pair pulses a read current through the selected word line. This causes all cores that were 1s to change state, inducing output signals on these sense lines; the bits that were 0s do not switch, giving negligible output. When executing a **write-call-store** instruction, the central processor places the contents of one of its registers on B9 and the call store writes this information in the location designated by the address on B8. For each bit there is a sense amplifier, which amplifies the signal and sets the output information in the data register.

A **clear-write** sequence is similar, except for the fact that the sense amplifiers are not used and the new information is placed in the data register from the central processor. The new information is written into the memory by using the contents of the data register to control the digit drivers. On a **read-call-store** instruction, the call store puts the contents of the storage location addressed by bus B8 on bus B10, and the central processor accepts this information in an internal register.

The call store is an extension of the central processor storage registers. At the end of some small job, it is often necessary for the central processor to move information out of the way for future reference. In the call store, we find information about dialed digits, availability of trunk and service circuits, and many other forms of data which change frequently. The importance of the call store is indicated by the fact that 20 percent of the central processor instructions are **reads** and **writes** for that store.

THE STORED PROGRAM

In a fully stored-program exchange all communication functions, from the initial detection of a call origination to the final release of network connections, are performed under the control of stored program. Subsystems and telephonic devices are designed to facilitate program control and to provide a convenient interface between the stored program and the real-time environment. The entire program is placed in the directly addressable instruction store, which is also referred to as the program store. The central processor communicates directly with the network control and with all other telephony-related devices through the input detector and the output generator subsystems. Each line, trunk, receiver, sender, operator position, perforator, and typewriter has input detector scanpoints associated with it. Inputs to the program (state changes) are collected from these devices via the scanpoints. The program controls the actions (states) of each device by manipulating the appropriate flip-flop associated with it in the output generator subsystem. The size of the stored program is primarily a function of the number of features designed into it and is practically independent of hardware quantities—that is, number of lines, trunks, etc. The call-processing portion consists of a little less than 12,000 instructions.

Origination and Signaling Programs

Calls enter the exchange via incoming toll trunks, extended area service trunks, operator trunks, and local subscriber lines. Each source is treated as a separate trunk, or line group, whose busy-idle status is monitored periodically by scans. In the scanning process appropriate input detector scanpoints are sampled to detect service requests and initiate network connections to the proper data-receiving devices. To accomodate the variety of signaling modes, the exchange contains multifrequency, dual-frequency, Touch-Tone, and dc receivers, as well as multifrequency and dc senders. Outputs of receivers are fed to input detector scanpoints and the inputs to senders originate from output-generator flip-flops. Separate programs collect digits from multifrequency, dual-frequency, and Touch-Tone receivers and from dial pulses from dc sources. Outpulsing is performed by other programs in two ways. For multifrequency sending, an entire digit is set up on a group of output generator flip-flops for a specified interval. DC outpulsing consists of setting and resetting a single flip-flop the proper number of times for each digit at specified make-break intervals and interdigital pauses.

Digit Analysis and Translation Programs

All digits collected by the exchange are analyzed by a digit-analysis section of the stored program to detect valid and invalid digit combinations. The program recognizes prefix digits, area codes, office codes, directory numbers, and special-service codes. With the assistance of translation programs the equipment required to extend or complete the call is identified and selected. Also the program sets the proper network connections in motion. To process the broad range of system call types involves a number of common conversion and equipment selection functions. The stored program contains the following translation programs: line translation; trunk or service circuit group translation; and programs of translation for area codes, office codes, directory numbers, toll rates and recent changes as well as for trunk terminal numbers, automatic number identification, memory location, automatic call transfer, and repertory dialing.

Network and Trunk-Control Programs

Operational requirements are met with six **connect programs** and five **disconnect** programs, each of which presents the network control with an order to perform an operation in the sequence. With other programs, they maintain data on existing connections in the process store, retry a connection in the event of blocking, and maintain waiting queues of connects and disconnects during periods of heavy traffic. Trunk types in the exchange consist of tone, revertive ringing, operator, intraoffice, extended area service, and toll trunks. Calling-and called-end supervision is provided for these trunks by a collection of programs which perform the following state-detection, timing, and control functions: answer and hang-up detection, answer-grace timing, no-answer timing, coin-toll initial-fee timing, coin-collect and return control, permanent signal with partial dial timing, disconnect timing, guard timing, no-hangup timing, code ringing, and operator rering and flashing control. A portion of the stored program performs automatic toll-ticketing functions. Single-entry ticketing data is punched on paper tape in standard format, with slight modifications to accommodate third-party and credit card numbers. Thus, no physical ticketer or tabulator hardware is employed.

Main Program

An executive program which controls the time-sharing of the central processor among the various sections of the stored program, also performs all program scheduling, priority selections and time distribution functions. Much of the stored program is implemented as a collection of periodically executed programs, each of which performs a small telephony task for all members of a particular type of equipment. As an example, one program detects originations on subcriber lines, another collects tones from Touch-Tone receivers, and another performs disconnect timing of trunks. Altogether there are approximately 40 such programs with execution rates ranging from once every 10 msec to once every 30 seconds. The basic scheduling technique used by the main program is illustrated symbolically in Fig. 9-4. Each lettered rectangle represents a periodically executed program. These programs are grouped according to frequency of execution and ordered in a list. Every 10 msec the main program sequences through the list from top to bottom, passing control to one program in each group. Figure 9-5 shows the effect as a function of time. Programs are shown in their order of execution and 10 msec intervals are indicated. Thus, program 1 is executed once every 10 msec; programs 2 and 3 are executed once every 20 msec; 4, 5, and 6 are executed once every 30 msec; and so on.

Program Coding and Assembly

The central processor executes instructions, and the memories store instructions which are 32 bits in length and

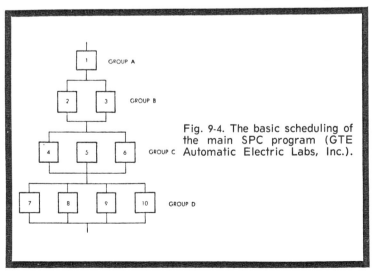

Fig. 9-4. The basic scheduling of the main SPC program (GTE Automatic Electric Labs, Inc.).

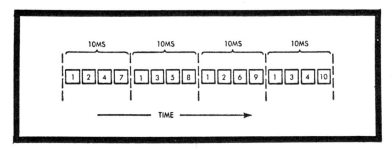

Fig. 9-5. Timing of program execution (GTE Automatic Electric Labs, Inc.).

binary in format. Programing in this binary machine language is too difficult to employ on a large scale. The standard computer industry solution to this problem is to provide a symbolic language for program coding. Then an assembler or compiler program is employed to perform the systematic task of converting symbolic statements into binary formats. This computer-oriented approach was used for this exchange by designing a suitable symbolic language for programer use. It allows memory locations to be referred to symbolically and provides a symbolic equivalent for each central processor-instruction as well as special statements for performing such tasks as allocating a range of process store words to a trunk group, defining the beginning and size of a translation store table, and creating the table constants (classes of service, directory numbers, trunk terminal numbers, toll rates, repertory dialing lists, etc.). An assembler program was developed to process the symbolic instructions, memory references, and special statements. In addition, this program was provided with the ability to identify programer coding errors and ambiguities— incorrectly written instructions and symbolic names referring to more than one memory location, for example.

Program Testing and Evaluation

With the assistance of two separate programs, it was possible to test and evaluate the programs of this exchange offline. One of these programs simulated the functional behavior of the central processor, memories, output generator, input detector, network, trunks, receivers, senders, service circuits, operator positions, perforator, and console typewriter. The other, a data compiler, provided a language with the ability to specify any combination of valid and invalid subscriber calls, operator actions, and internal system conditions such as network blocking and equipment queuing. Both of these programs were developed to operate on an IBM 7094 computer. Their interrelationship with the assembler is shown in Fig. 9-6.

The assembler program converted the symbolically described stored program into a special encoded form. The data compiler program converted symbolically described test calls into events—originations, disconnects, dial pulses, etc.—occurring at various points in time. The simulator executed the encoded stored program using time-sequenced call events as input data. Debugging facilities were designed specifically for the testing of a real-time control program. The programer was provided with flexible controls to selectively record, as a function of time or space, any detail of stored-program or subsystem operation during simulated processing of test calls.

Logical errors and timing problems uncovered during simulation were removed from the stored program by symbolically coding corrections and repeating the assembly-simulation sequence. As the correct handling of various calls was verified, new tests were coded symbolically and processed through the data compiler and simulator. When the program could not be made to fail during simulated processing of multiple calls, the binary output of the assembler was generated and placed into the program store of the exchange to make ready for online operation. The use of programed simulation permitted the removal of 85 percent of the logical errors and timing problems from the stored

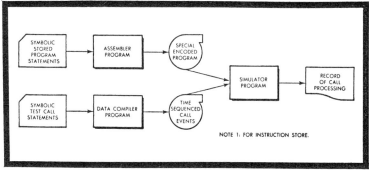

Fig. 9-6. The interrelationship of test programs with the assembler (GTE Automatic Electric Labs, Inc.).

program prior to the system integration of hardware and software.

SPC MEMORY TECHNOLOGY

In common stored-program-controlled exchanges, three basic types of memory systems are of interest:

1. In the **destructive readout type**, the contents of the memory are destroyed when it is interrogated by a read pulse. The insertion of information into this system requires the use of a write pulse with information available from input registers. In such memories toroidal ferrite cores are commonly used, but in the future, semiconductor memories using MOS techniques may compete for this application.

2. In the **nondestructive-readout, mechanically alterable** type, the information is inserted, stored, and changed by some mechanical operation. A read pulse and an input address are required to interrogate this memory, but no write pulse is required. An example of such a memory is the card-changeable twistor magnetic memory found in the ESS exchanges of the Bell System.

3. In the **nondestructive-readout, electrically alterable** type, only a read pulse and an address are required as in (2) above. However, this memory differs from that of (2) in that its stored information can be changed electrically instead of mechanically. Examples of such memories are the piggyback twistor and the plated-wire memory. The former is used in Bell's TSPS system and the Canadian SP-1 SPC exchange while the latter is used in the Japanese D-10 system.

The Destructive-Readout Type

In all SPC exchanges currently in use or in field trials, the destructive-readout type of memory is used in the call store, because it requires only a temporary memory—sometimes referred to as a **scratch pad memory**. As mentioned above, most SPC exchanges use ferrite cores for this purpose. However, in Bell's No. 2 ESS and in the early production of the No. 1 ESS a **ferrite-sheet memory** was used in this application. The basic device here is a 1-inch square ferrite sheet approximately 30 mils thick, with a 16x16 array of 25-mil-diameter holes located on 50-mil centers. The material used is a mixed magnesium-manganese ferrite similar to that used in square-loop toroids but with a higher Curie point, which provides an extended temperature range. Each hole, when excited by coincident-current pulses of about 250 mA, acts as a square-loop memory core with a field constrained to the annular region immediately surrounding each hole. Thus, in principle the ferrite sheet does not differ from those memories using separate ferrite cores. Four electrical conductors are associated with the ferrite sheet. One serves to link all of the holes on a sheet, while the other three combine to form a standard coincident-current access explained in more detail below.

Background for Core Storage

The fundamental operation of a magnetic memory element can be described best by referring to its hysteresis loop, which is a plot of the relationship between the applied magnetic field and the magnetization state of a core. In a typical hysteresis loop, shown in Fig. 9-7, it is seen that the magnetization can take one of two stable states (labeled a and b) in the absence of an applied magnetic field. These two states can be used to store information as a logic 1 or 0. To use the core as a memory element, the toroid is linked by two or more wires threaded through its aperture.

A core is read by the application of a full read current, $-I3$, which is sufficient to switch the core to reset state **a.** If the core is set to the 1 state before application of the read current, there will be a large change in the flux, which induces a voltage on the wires linking the core. This voltage is amplified and used to set an information-register flip-flop. If the core is set to the 0 state, there will be only a small flux change resulting in the production of a correspondingly small voltage, which is rejected by a threshold stage in the sense amplifier. A 0 is sensed in this case.

The square-loop properties of the core can be used to allow the core to perform address selection as well as storage. If a partial current, $I1$, which is less than the threshold, $I2$, is applied, switching will not occur. If twice the value is applied, the core can switch. By using the wiring arrangement of Fig. 9-7B and injecting a current $I1$ into both one **X** wire and one **Y** wire, the addition of these currents at their intersection to a

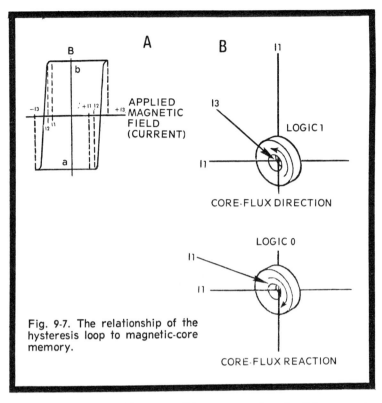

Fig. 9-7. The relationship of the hysteresis loop to magnetic-core memory.

full current, I3, will cause this core and only this core to switch. By this means two dimensions of selection can be achieved. The induced voltage in the sense wire (Fig. 8-9) will store a 1 or a 0.

The incoming address information, which is held in an address register, is used to turn on one selector switch in each of four groups: positive X, negative X, positive Y, and negative Y. Each of these switches is duplicated for read and write, since current is required in one direction through the X and Y wires for reading and in the other direction for writing. After each read operation, all cores in the selected word will have been switched to the 0 state. A so-called **inhibit driver** will be turned on during the write phase of a store cycle for each bit in which it is required to store a 0. This causes a further half-select current to oppose the effects of the X and Y currents. For each bit where there is no such current, the X and Y currents will combine to reverse the effect of the read phase and leave the selected core in a 1 state.

This background leads us to a so-called 3D system (X, Y, and inhibit-sense), which was described first in 1951. Some years later, a word-select system (2D), which removed the selection function from the storage matrix and put it into the peripheral drive circuitry, was devised. This arrangement resulted in a higher speed, but costs were increased due to the greatly increased number of drive circuit components. In the mid-1950s a compromise system called 2½D was developed in which the Y coordinate of core selection was removed from the weaving of the stack and combined with inhibit-sense.

Such systems use three wires per core where high speed is required, and two where large capacity and low cost are desired. Either arrangement is attractive as a fast store for several reasons. Costs are reduced by the removal of the fourth wire; the wires can be of somewhat larger diameter with lower resistance; wire terminations are fewer; cores per wire are fewer, resulting in lower drive voltages and the use of lower-cost transistors. Also, faster cycle times are possible for a given core because there is no digit-noise recovery time. For these reasons the 2½D organization for core stores has become popular. A typical application is found in Automatic Electric's No. 1 EAX SPC exchange. Bell Laboratories has gone even a step further toward simplification and is using a 2D organization in a redesigned version of the No. 1 ESS. In this application they are using some 850,000 ferrite cores in the call store to replace the ferrite sheets, which were used in the initial versions of No. 1 ESS.

Semiconductor Memories

Prior to the advent of LSI (large scale integration) technologies, semiconductor memories were too high in cost to be considered as a replacement for magnetic-core storage devices. However, with the new technologies it is thought likely that semiconductor memories will play a much greater role in the not too distant future. They offer significant speed increases over various magnetic memories, as well as size and compatibility advantages with the possible provision of logic within the memory. They have the disadvantages of volatility and higher power dissipation. However, by using backup stores of the magnetic-disk or drum type, the fact that memory can be lost with a power failure can be tolerated.

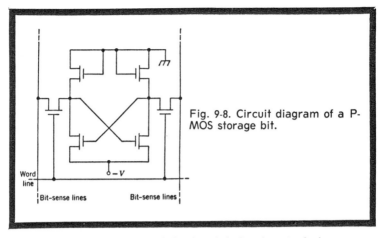

Fig. 9-8. Circuit diagram of a P-MOS storage bit.

Word line

Bit-sense lines   Bit-sense lines

−V

Although a number of device fabrication techniques are available to the integrated circuit designer in the production of semiconductor memories, P-MOS (P-channel, metal-oxide) and N-MOS (N-channel, metal-oxide) techniques have received the most attention. It should be understood that semiconductor memories are basically like flip-flops. The diagram for a P-channel, enhancement-mode, MOS storage bit indicates this in Fig. 9-8. Figure 9-9 shows what is meant by a P-channel MOS transistor.

It is beyond the scope of this book to go into extensive details about the production of LSI memories and their equivalent circuitry. However, it will suffice to say here that in some applications the production of P-channel silicon-gate structures is much the same as that for N-channel devices. In a typical case for N-channel devices (Fig. 9-10), the starting wafer is boron-doped, P-type silicon. Fabrication starts with

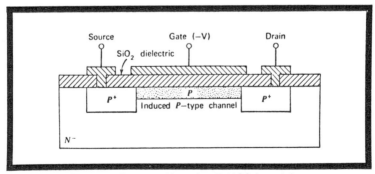

Fig. 9-9. Cross section of a P-MOS transistor.

the P-type wafers being thermally oxidized to a thickness of about 1 micron, followed by parts of the oxide being removed to define the gate and diffusion regions in the first five photomasking steps. After this, a gate dielectric and a polycrystalline silicon are deposited, after which areas defining the gate regions of the transistors and the silicon undercrossing are etched out by photomasking. Then there is a diffusion operation in which N-type impurities form the source and drain regions and the diffused undercrossing.

At this time it appears that N-channel MOS memories have the greatest promise to replace magnetic core memories. Compared with P-MOS memories they are 2 to 3 times faster (100 nsec) ; 2 to 4 times denser (4000 to 8000 bits ∕ chip); have a generally lower threshold voltage than P-MOS (2 to 5V) and are potentially less expensive (100 bits ∕ cent). The fact that N carriers have higher mobility than P carriers accounts for the speed ratios. Because of reduced parasitic conduction, reduced spacing between memory elements, narrower line widths, and smaller contact holes, memory elements are smaller and can be more closely spaced. Typically N-MOS had widths and spacings of 0.2 mil, while P- MOS dimensions are 0.6 mil.

The Nondestructive Readout Type

During the first decade of SPC exchange development it was thought that the program store must be of the semipermanent or so-called **fixed** type. Initially, it was necessary to use mechanically alterable stores for this purpose, because electrically alterable ones had not yet been developed. The best known example of the former is the permanent-magnet

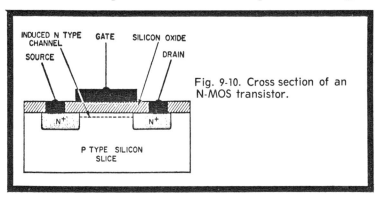

Fig. 9-10. Cross section of an N-MOS transistor.

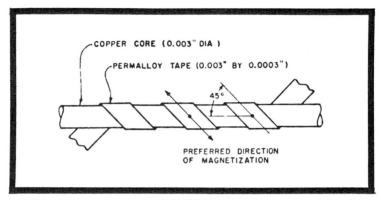

COPPER CORE (0.003" DIA.)

PERMALLOY TAPE (0.003" BY 0.0003")

45°

PREFERRED DIRECTION
OF MAGNETIZATION

Fig. 9-11. A basic twistor element (GTE Automatic Electric Labs, Inc.).

twistor memory used in the program stores of the Bell System's No. 1 ESS, No. 2 ESS, and No. 101 ESS exchanges. Perhaps, it is a misnomer to say that it is mechanically altered. However, the program card must be removed from the program store physically and then altered magnetically to change the program.

The Permanent-Magnet Twistor. The **twistor** gets it name from the fact that a current-carrying wire in a magnetic field tends to twist so that the magnitude and direction of the twist is directly dependent upon the magnetic field. A typical twistor element is fabricated by wrapping a thin magnetic tape around a core of copper wire as shown in Fig. 9-11. The most basic twistor memory consists of a short length of twistor surrounded by a wirewound solenoid. The winding of the solenoid is at right angles to the core of the twistor as shown in Fig. 9-12. Switching of the tape is accomplished by a current flowing through the twistor core wire, current flowing in the solenoid, or a combination of the two in coincidence. However, in the Bell Laboratories ESS design the twistor is switched by the absence of the magnetic fields of small vicalloy magnets on the program cards which are placed in close proximity to the twistor cells. Magnetic flux in the permalloy tape wraps helically around the twistor wire and links both the wire and a copper strap which forms the twistor cell at every intersection. Since the flux path is closed through the air, the twistor cell is sensitive to adjacent magnetic fields. If the vicalloy magnet on the program card has a strong magnetic field, it will affect the operation of the twistor cell. If the spot over the twistor cell is not magnetized, the field due to a current pulse in the copper strap will reverse the magnetization and cause the twistor cell to switch. Then a voltage pulse in the twistor wire will be read as a binary 1. However, if the spot is magnetized by the presence of a small vicalloy magnet its external field saturates the permalloy tape at the intersection and the pulse in the copper strap cannot reverse the magnetization of the twistor cell. This voltage is read as a binary 0.

Random access to any word in the twistor memory is provided by connecting each copper strap to a ferrite core in a matrix of biased core switches. These switches operate very much like the cores of a coincident core memory. Two sets of access windings (one running parallel to the planes, the other perpendicular to them) connect the switches to the memory

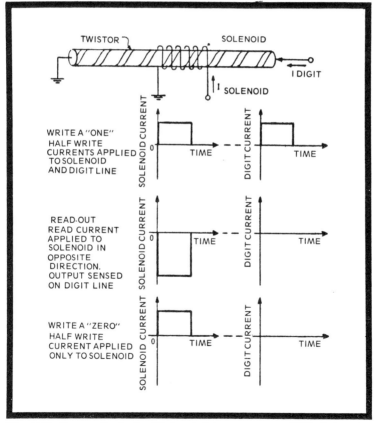

Fig. 9-12. One method of utilizing twistor memory (GTE Automatic Electric Labs, Inc.).

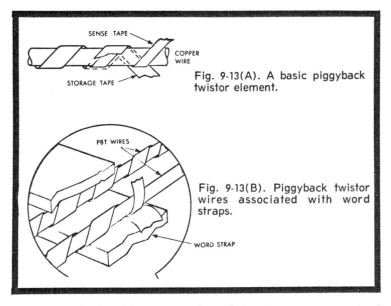

Fig. 9-13(A). A basic piggyback twistor element.

Fig. 9-13(B). Piggyback twistor wires associated with word straps.

input terminals. The core selected by the two energized windings acts as a current transformer to generate the current pulse in the copper strap.

With the permanent-magnet twistor, information is stored in the tiny vicalloy permanent magnets, mentioned above, which are mounted on aluminum program cards. To change any information it is necessary to remove the appropriate program card and to change the magnetization of these tiny magnets under writing heads in a **card writer**. The card is then replaced. This procedure has the disadvantage of being slow and of placing stringent requirements on the positioning of the magnets and their corresponding twistor wires.

The Piggyback Twistor. In a modification of the basic twistor construction, a magnetic storage tape is wound on top of the sense tape as shown in Fig. 9-13. Thus, the name **piggyback** is used to describe this type of twistor, and the abbreviation **PBT** is employed. Pairs of PBT wires are located between so-called **word-strap** conductors. A write operation is accomplished by applying a word strap current at the same time that bit-current pulses are circulating around the loops formed by the PBT pairs. The direction of circulation of each bit current determines the binary state that will be written at the selected word. Clockwise bit currents write binary 1s, while counterclockwise currents write binary 0s. These bit currents are obtained from write-current generators connected to the ends of each PBT loop and word-strap access currents are derived from the access matrix.

In a read operation, the bits of binary information stored at a memory location are used to generate signals at detector circuits connected to the ends of each PBT pair. The operation is accomplished by applying about half as much current as is used for write operations to the desired word strap. The magnetic field generated by this current overcomes the static field from the storage-tape magnets and causes one of the two sensing segments of the bit to switch its magnetization. Only one of the sensing elements is switched, because the second one is already aligned with the read field. This comes about because the sense tape is magnetically soft enough to be aligned by the field lines emanating from the storage segment above it. In the very short time (about one-millionth of a second) required for the segment being switched to reverse its magnetization, a voltage is generated across the ends of the PBT pair. The polarity of this voltage depends on which of the two sensing segments was switched—or on the information that was stored during the previous write operation. When the read field is switched off, the static fields from the storage magnets restore the sensing elements to their original state and the cycle is complete. The applied field for reading is strong enough to overcome the static field from a storage magnet, but is not strong enough to change the magnetization of the magnet itself. This nondestructive-readout feature makes it unnecessary to rewrite the original information after reading it. Also, as seen above, the program is electrically alterable—the need for program cards is eliminated and changes may be written in from a teletypewriter with the proper connecting equipment.

Plated-Wire Memories. Abbreviated as **PSM**, for **plated-wire semipermanent memory**, this is another technique that provides an electrically alterable store. The magnetic material for PSM is composed of a ferromagnetic thin film, easily magnetized in only the circumferential direction, and plated onto 0.1 mm Be-Cu wire. The ferromagnetic film is composed of three 2500A-thick permalloy films and two 600A-thick Ni-Co films which are electrolytically plated in five layers. A matrix consists of crosspoints of plated and word wires perpendicular to each other. One such crosspoint is

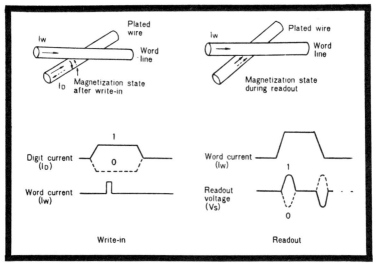

Fig. 9-14(A). Arrangement to utilize plated-wire memory (Nippon Telegraph and Telephone Public Corp.).

shown in Fig. 9-14. It also is seen from this figure that write operations are realized through the use of digit and word currents. Read operations are effected by driving the word current which results in the direction of magnetization being oriented from the circumferential direction to along the plated wire. Changing the direction of magnetization induces voltage in the plated wire with a polarity which varies depending upon whether the information is 1 or 0.

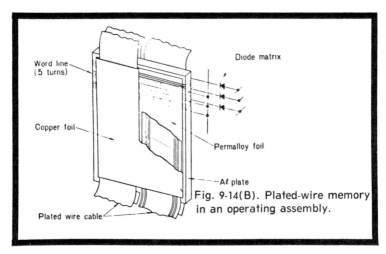

Fig. 9-14(B). Plated-wire memory in an operating assembly.

184

Typical SPC Exchanges and the New Services

10

Although the Bell System investigated electronic techniques for exchange switching from 1945 and employed a magnetic-drum memory in the common control of an experimental exchange in the early 1950s, a stored-program exchange was not field-tested until 1960. During that year the Morris electronic exchange, which incorporated all the basic principles of stored-program control, was placed in operation in Morris, Illinois, to serve some 600 subscriber lines. As shown in Fig. 10-1, the major sections of the switching system are very little different than those found in present-day SPC exchanges. However, the components in the sections were considerably different. Gas-tube crosspoints were used in the speech-path switching network; a barrier-grid electrostatic storage tube provided the temporary memory or call store, and a flying-spot store provided the semipermanent memory of the program store. After the test trials of this exchange, only the stored-program concept remained unchanged in further developments.

As No. 1 ESS emerged from the Bell Laboratories, a form of reed relay called the **ferreed** replaced the gas-tubes as crosspoints in the speech-path network. In the memories, ferrite sheets replaced the barrier-grid electrostatic storage tube in the call store, and the twistor replaced the flying-spot memory in the program store. Also, the system organization and the organization of the program itself were changed from that of the Morris installation. The change from the gas-tube crosspoints was made largely because of their inability to carry either high amplitude 20 Hz ringing signals or direct current from the subscriber lines. Solid-state crosspoints in the form of PNPN diodes were appealing substitutes for the gas tubes but they too suffered from the same deficiencies relative to ringing signal and direct current from the telephone lines. The metallic path provided by the reed-relay combination was the answer to these problems despite its slower switching speed.

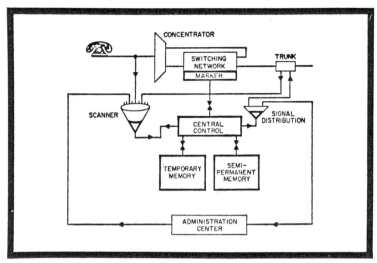

Fig. 10-1. Block diagram of Morris electronic SPC exchange.

In the call store, the ferrite sheet memory was chosen over the barrier-grid tube because it can store a longer word, is more economical, and has greater potential reliability. In the program store, the twistor memory was chosen because it did not have the high-voltage and hot-cathode problems of the flying-spot store, its 6 million-bit capacity was adequate and offered the increased reliability of a solid-state device. In another area of the system, the line-scanning components of the Morris exchange were replaced by unique, saturable-ferrite-core transformers—called **ferrods**—in which two solenoid windings over a rectangular ferrite stick were connected in a balanced arrangement on each side of a subscriber's line to sense the off-hook condition. Since the earliest versions of the No. 1 ESS exchange, the ferreeds and the ferrods have continued to be used, but there have been some changes in the memory components as described in Chapter 9.

THE NO. 1 ESS SWITCHING SYSTEM

To realize translation and control economies, speech-path switch and grid sizes were adopted to fit the binary nature of the ESS control language. Possible binary switch sizes would be 4x4, 8x8, 16x16, etc. However, 8x8 arrays were chosen as the best compromise due in part to the cost of the ferreed crosspoints. These arrays were organized into 16 grids such as the 8x8 grid of Fig. 10-2. This configuration provides every line with full access to the 1024 junctors (8x8x16). From this organization four stages of switching are built up on both the line-link network and the trunk-link networks, as shown in Fig. 10-3, to give a total of eight stages for the No. 1 ESS system. This plan is a compromise between economy of crosspoints, complexity, and maximal size. For example, a network of 4x4 arrays would contain fewer crosspoints, but more stages would be needed to attain the same maximal network size and equivalent blocking performance. So the saving in crosspoints would be offset by more complex wiring and control requirements.

Since the No. 1 ESS system is for large-exchange applications, any network up to a maximum of 64,000 lines and 16,000 trunks may be assembled from these basic units. Link networks are connected through the junctors to establish paths for the three common types of central office calls—intraoffice, interoffice, and tandem. A novel feature of the No. 1 ESS network is that intraoffice calls through intraoffice junctors bypass the trunk-link network. The junctor circuits extend battery circuits and supervisory signaling circuits to these calls. All other traffic is connected to the battery and

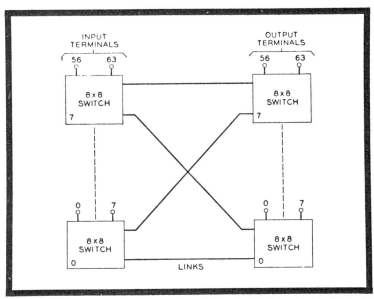

Fig. 10-2. Switching grid of ferreed matrixes in No. 1 ESS (Bell Systems Technical Journal).

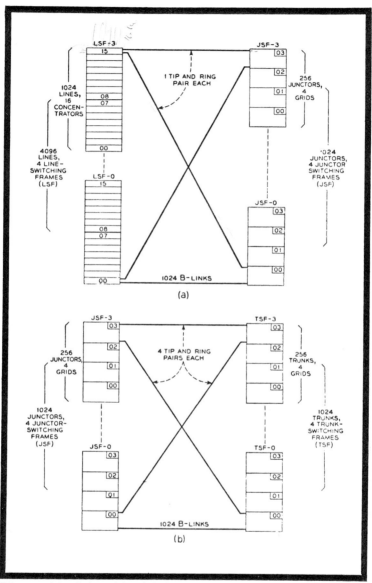

Fig. 10-3. Line-link and trunk-link networks of No. 1 ESS (Bell Systems Technical Journal).

supervised at the trunk circuits. Line traffic is concentrated in the first two stages of the line-link network. In a typical No. 1 ESS office, 64 lines have access to only 16 second-stage links. This 2-stage, four-to-one concentrator configuration is uniquely efficient in its use of crosspoints, requiring only six per line. Thus, its traffic performance equals or surpasses that of previous 4-to-1 concentrators which typically require 10 crosspoints per line.

Most of the elements of the No. 1 ESS stored-program system have been described in other parts of this book, so it will suffice here to say that its operation depends upon the same general principles as those outlined for the SPC exchange in Chapter 9. Its central processor, with 13,000 logic circuits incorporating 60,000 semiconductors, works in conjunction with basic call stores having a capacity of 196,608 bits and basic program stores having a capacity of 131,000 words. However, both stores can be increased to accommodate larger offices. The storage needs for the data, which goes into the program store, ranges from 1 to 14 million bits depending upon the office size.

There are at least five types of No. 1 ESS offices in service. Four types of 2-wire offices are in large, medium-sized and Centrex spplications, while one type of 4-wire office is in service in the Autovon military application. The four 2-wire types are classified as central control (CC) and signal processor (SP), the CC Centrex and the SP Centrex offices. The central control version of No. 1 ESS is the original version. The signal processor version uses the addition of equipment to take over many of the repetitive functions required in scanning lines and collecting dialed digits to increase the traffic-handling capacity of the office. The first SP version was installed in New York City in 1968. Since then most of the ESS offices installed in large metropolitan centers have been with signal processors.

As shown in Fig. 10-4, the signal processor is an integral part of the exchange. Like the central processor it receives and processes information from stored data. However, it is only about two-thirds the size of the central control and requires only call stores of its own to perform its relatively simple tasks. These functions include interrogating the peripheral system for inputs such as dial pulses, customer-service requests, Touch-Tone digits, or teletypewriter characters—and loading these inputs into input buffers, called **hoppers**, where they are picked up and processed by the central control. Also, the signal processor receives information from the central control via output buffers and responds by carrying out tasks such as relaying orders to the

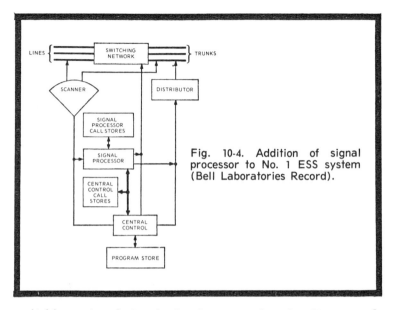

Fig. 10-4. Addition of signal processor to No. 1 ESS system (Bell Laboratories Record).

switching network, trunk circuits or service circuits; recording information on **AMA (automatic message accounting)** magnetic tape; or sending multifrequency signals to distant exchanges. It is in this way that the signal processor relieves the central control of routine work and frees it to perform more complex tasks.

Centrex service, which is really a PABX application in which much of the exchange equipment remains in the central office, was first offered with No. 1 ESS in 1968. One of the largest such installations is in the Pentagon building in Washington, D.C., where 17,000 lines are switched and 74 consoles of equipment are involved.

THE NO. 2 ESS SWITCHING SYSTEM

The basic objective in the design of the No. 2 ESS office (Fig. 10-5) was to provide a stored-program switching system which would be economically viable in a range of 1,000 to 10,000 subscriber lines. Much of the design was derived from the No. 1 ESS and the No. 101 ESS. The switching network is made up of ferreed switches of the type used in the No. 1 ESS and other peripheral equipment is similar. However, the No. 2 ESS control equipment is based more on that of the No. 101 ESS.

Processor Frame

The processor frame is a 7 x 4 ft unit containing the program control (instruction-processing logic), a semiautonomous input-output section, capacity for 16,384 call-store words of 16 bits each, and capacity for 512 bipolar central-pulse distributor points. The call store may be equipped in steps of 4096 words, while the central pulse distributor may be equipped, as required with packages of 8 points. High-speed transistor-resistor logic, employing thermocompression bonded-beam-leaded silicon devices with thin-film resistors on a ceramic base, is used for all logic applications in this frame.

The basic program and translation store frame contains 4 permanent-magnet twistor modules with a total capacity of 65,536 words of 22 bits. In addition to this basic frame, growth frames are available to permit expansion of this store in steps of 16,384 words to a maximum size of 262,144 words. The format used for instructions contained within the program store, which consists of two types, is the same as that used in the No. 1 ESS. Type 1 uses a 22-bit word, which contains a 5-bit operation code and a 16-bit address plus a check bit. Type 2

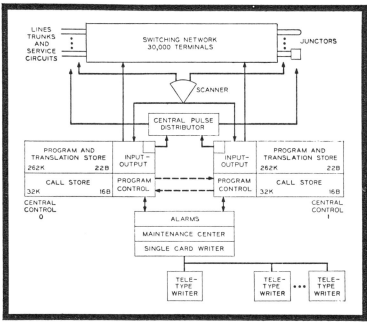

Fig. 10-5. Block diagram of No. 2 ESS (Bell Systems Technical Journal).

contains two complete 10-bit instructions, each of which contains a 5-bit address and a 5-bit operation code. The short 5-bit address is made effective by extensive use of relative and implicit addressing of both program and call-store information. This format was chosen for No. 1 ESS and No. 101 ESS because of its high efficiency and low cost.

A semiautonomous **input-output (I-O) unit** is included in each central control. This unit shares the call store with the program control on generally lower-priority basis. This I-O unit works together with the program for the scanning of line originations, collection of dialed digits and tone signals, outpulsing, and data transmission. The use of the I-O unit for digit receiving and sending functions has allowed the normal interrupt cycle to be set at 25 msec rather than the usually required faster cycle of 5 to 10 msec. In addition, the precise timing and short scan intervals available through the use of the I-O unit has allowed simplification of in circuits such as incoming trunks from step-by-step offices.

Program Instructions

Microprograms are used for program instructions. With this kind of instructions a major feature is that very few bits are wasted on unused options and unneeded address words, as is often the case with larger program instruction words. The use of general-purpose registers within the temporary memory for all types of calls has resulted in program and administrative simplifications. These registers consist of a progress mark, which defines the state of the call, plus other information pertinent to the particular call. All call registers containing progress marks use the same format and the same register size, allowing common programs to be used for many different call states. The progress marks themselves define the first address of the program required to process the particular call. The preponderance of call processing can then be described as a series of transfers to the individual progress-mark programs. In addition to straightforward call-processing techniques, great emphasis has been placed on the use of subroutines. Many progress-mark programs consist entirely of calls to common subroutines. Some special orders and pushdown-list features have been included in the basic instruction repertoire to aid in the writing and facilitate the use of subroutines.

AUTOMATIC ELECTRIC'S NO. 1 EAX

The initial installation of the No. 1 EAX system was successfully cut into service in 1972. Although it is capable of serving up to 20,000 lines and 30,000 directory numbers, the first installation serves 4,000 lines. This system is structured around wired-logic markers and register-senders for network control and interface, and on-line data-processing units for stored-program control of call-processing and system diagnostics. This system follows more recent trends in the design of the program store in that core storage with backup is provided. The system divides into switching network and common-control subsystems.

Switching Network

In the network sybsystem the line group is a 4-stage switching network of correed crosspoints. The stages are designated A, B, C, and R. For an originating call, the A and B stages are used to set up a path from the line inlet to one of 140 originating junctors, while the R stage is used to provide a temporary signaling path between the originating junctors and 1 of 20 register junctors. The originating junctors provide a separate path to the register junctors for receiving and sending, and the register junctors provide the interface with the originator once the originating path is established. For a terminating call, the A, B, and C stages are used to set up a path from one of 120 terminating junctors which provide ringing control, battery feed, and call supervision to 1 of the 1000 line inlets. The originating and terminating junctors remain connected in the talking path for the duration of the call. The remainder of the network subsystem is composed of the trunk register group and the selector group.

Common Control

In Fig. 10-6 is shown a basic configuration of the No. 1 EAX and connection of most of the elements of the common-control subsystem with the switching-network blocks. The originating marker detects calls for service in the line group and the trunk-register group, and controls the selection of idle paths and the establishment of connections. On incoming trunk calls, this marker detects calls for service in the incoming

193

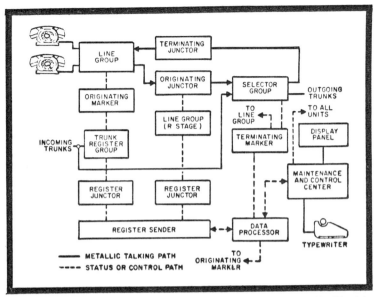

Fig. 10-6. Block diagram of No. 1 EAX system (GTE Automatic Electric Labs, Inc.).

trunks connected to a trunk-register group, and controls path selection between incoming trunks and register junctors. On both line originations and incoming trunk originations, the originating marker interfaces with the data processor and provides to the stored program the identity of the originator and the identity of the selected junctors. These markers are duplicated and arranged in pairs, with each capable of processing separate calls simultaneously under nonfault conditions.

The terminating marker sets up all calls through the selector group and, in the case of a line termination, through the line group as well. Under the direction of the stored program executed through the central processor, the terminating marker connects the inlet of the selector group to an idle trunk or junctor circuit. The stored program specifies the group of outlets, and the terminating marker selects the idle outlet, either randomly or sequentially, as directed by the stored program. The terminating markers are duplicated and arranged in pairs, with jobs alternating between the units of a pair.

The register-sender is a time-shared unit with the ability to register and process 192 calls simultaneously from local lines and incoming trunks. It provides the logic and memory equipment for receiving and storing incoming digits, and the pulse-generating circuitry to forward a call toward its destination. It utilizes a ferrite-core memory for information storage and for interfacing with the data processor. The register-sender common logic and memory are duplicated, and operate in synchronous mode for instantaneous error and fault detection.

The data processor unit is composed of a computer complex and a drum-memory complex. The former consists of

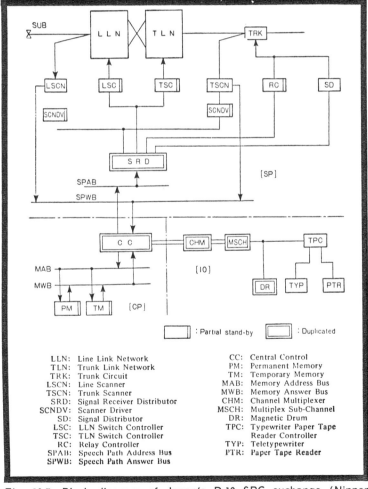

LLN: Line Link Network
TLN: Trunk Link Network
TRK: Trunk Circuit
LSCN: Line Scanner
TSCN: Trunk Scanner
SRD: Signal Receiver Distributor
SCNDV: Scanner Driver
SD: Signal Distributor
LSC: LLN Switch Controller
TSC: TLN Switch Controller
RC: Relay Controller
SPAB: Speech Path Address Bus
SPWB: Speech Path Answer Bus

CC: Central Control
PM: Permanent Memory
TM: Temporary Memory
MAB: Memory Address Bus
MWB: Memory Answer Bus
CHM: Channel Multiplexer
MSCH: Multiplex Sub-Channel
DR: Magnetic Drum
TPC: Typewriter Paper Tape
     Reader Controller
TYP: Teletypewriter
PTR: Paper Tape Reader

Fig. 10-7. Block diagram of Japan's D-10 SPC exchange (Nippon Telegraph and Telephone Public Corp.).

Classification of services		Number	Items of service	Electronic switching system D-10	Crossbar switching system C400	Comments
New telephone services	Facilitation of dialing	1	Variable abbreviated dialing	●	●	
		2	Restriction of dialing range (DID, DOD)	● (CES only)	C410 ● (CES only)	
		3	International subscriber dialing	○		
	Facilitation of receiving	4	Telephone advisory message service	○	○	
		5	Transfer of terminating call	△		
		6	Automatic intercept service	●	●	Already presented with AIS
	Facilitation of conversing	7	Call-waiting service	●	●	
		8	Add-on	● (CES only)	C410 ● (CES only)	
		9	Holding	△	△	
	Facilitation of charging	10	Charge information system (visible)	○	○	
			Charge information system (audible)	○	○	
	Other	11	Centralized extension system	●	C410 ●	
New telecommunication services	Video telecommunication	12	Video telephone switching system	○		
	Public data communication	13	Telephone calculating	●	●	Named "DIALS"

●: Existing
○: To be finalized
△: Planned
AIS: Automatic Intercept Service
DIALS: Dendenkosha Immediate Arithmetic and Library Calculation System

Fig. 10-8. The new services as offered by both SPC exchanges and existing exchanges (Nippon Telegraph and Telephone Public Corp.).

a central processor, ferrite-core memory, computer memory control, and communications links. These communication links provide the central processor with information concerning its input-output devices, condition of the other subsystems and the processing of calls by the subsystems. The drum-memory complex provides mass storage for infrequently executed programs and for translations, utilizing magnetic drums with a capacity of 198,000 words of 27 bits each. The drum-memory complex provides for the transfer of programs and data directly to the core memory. Two of the data processor's input-output devices, the ticketing scanner and the magnetic tape unit, work in conjunction with the stored program to provide for local automatic message accounting as an available option. Other input-output devices include the communication register for communication with the markers, the teletypewriter, and the paper-tape equipment. The data processors are duplicated, with the computer complexes operating in synchronism, and the drum memory operating independently.

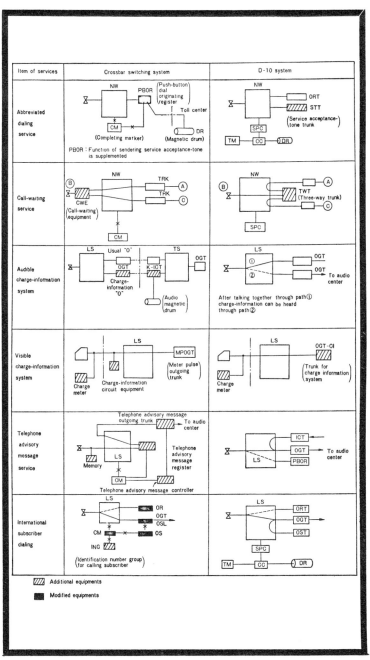

Fig. 10-9. Connections and modifications to provide the new services
(Nippon Telegraph and Telephone Corp.).

JAPAN'S D-10 SPC EXCHANGE AND THE NEW SERVICES

The new D-10 SPC exchange, a block diagram of which is shown in Fig. 10-7, offers many new services, as shown in Fig. 10-8. However, most of these services are either already provided by crossbar switching systems or can be provided by modifications of those systems as shown in Fig. 10-9. The electronic SPC method is to be preferred because with it only software needs to be changed for new services, while with the crossbar systems new or modified hardware needs to be added. Other advantages for the electronic SPC system are higher reliability with solid-state components, high-speed control (which shortens the connection time), and traffic control (which makes for more effective use of the existing network). Also, electronic switching makes possible the most economical use of equipment in common with the existing network rather than modifying it for all of the new services.

Experience also shows that in the case of Centrex, customer traffic is so heavy and the requirements so complicated that expanded service can be supplied easily only by the electronic switching system. Even with the D-10 local switching system, where the maximum capacity is about 40,000 subscribers when operating at 0.1 erlang per subscriber, the system's processing ability is substantially absorbed in Centrex service. When half of the system's processing ability is expended on Centrex service, the number of general subscribers which can be accommodated is reduced to about 10 percent, because of the many new services requiring the release-link operation and control of the lamps and keys on the attendant console to handle the calls directed to the operators.

Time-Division Switching Systems

11

The introduction of the T-1 carrier by the Bell System marked the first widespread application of time-division multiplexing and pulse-code modulation in commercial telephony. Actually, the T-1 carrier system is a transmission application and does not necessarily require time-division exchange switching. However, the rapid application of the T-1 systems and its associated D-1 channel bank to voice channels and the growth in the transmission of digital data makes its desirable to utilize digital exchange switching for compatibility and the advantages stemming from it. Using the D-1 channel bank, the T-1 system is capable of handling 24 voice channels simultaneously. The D-2 channel bank, which was developed primarily for toll trunks, provides better fidelity than D-1 and handles four times as many voice channels. Delivering four independent outputs, each of which is equivalent to the total output of a D-1 bank, the D-2 provides four 24-channel groups in a pulse stream of 1.544 megabits per second. In the new No. 4 ESS digital toll exchange of the Bell System, voice signals will remain in digital form if they enter from T-1 lines, or will be converted to digital form if they enter in analog form. Then they will be switched by a combined space and time-division system. Digital data from computers or other sources can also be handled directly by such a switching system without conversions.

Pulse modulation techniques are essential to time-division switching. It is by pulse modulation that a message can be arranged in time in such a way that several channels can be interleaved and switching can take place between these channels, which are separated in time rather than in space. Only pulse-amplitude modulation (PAM) and pulse-code modulation (PCM) are used in time-division switching systems.

Pulse modulation methods require such unique treatment of message signals that it is well to look at some of the fun-

199

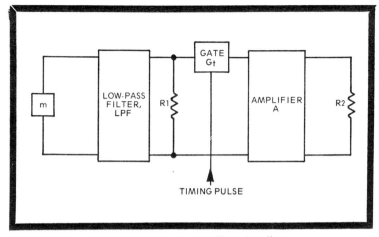

Fig. 11-1. Time-sampling circuit.

damental aspects of pulse-amplitude modulation and the steps leading to pulse-code modulation. Time sampling and multiplexing are essential to the formation of signals which can be subjected to time-division switching.

TIME SAMPLING

The block diagram of a typical time-sampling circuit is shown in Fig. 11-1. The message signal, m, is applied to a low-pass filter (whose purpose will be explained later) followed by termination in a resistance, R1. By interposing a gate, G_t, whose output is controlled by timing pulses, the signal at the input of amplifier A will result in a series of pulses varying with the amplitude of the message signal voltage, m, across its output load resistance, R2. Figure 11-2A shows the message voltage; Fig. 11-2B shows the timing pulses or sampling function, and Fig. 11-2C shows the pulse-amplitude modulated (PAM) waveform appearing across R2.

According to Nyquist's sampling theorem, if a message (a real, continuous function of time with a band-limited spectrum) is sampled at regular intervals and at a rate slightly higher than twice its highest frequency, the samples contain all of the information in the original message. It is for this reason that the low-pass filter is inserted in the circuit of Fig. 11-1 and the frequency of the timing pulses controlling the sampling gate, G_t, is set at approximately twice the highest signal frequency appearing at the output of the filter, LPF.

Mathematically, the sampling process can be considered as the multiplication of the message function of time, $m(t)$, by the periodic sampling function, $g(t)$. The latter can be represented by the general Fourier series as

$$g(t) \ \frac{g_0}{2} + \sum_{n=1}^{\infty} g_n \cos(n\omega t + \theta_n) \qquad (11\text{-}1)$$

where the spacing between pulses is $T = 1/f_0 \ 2 \ /w_0$. Then in linear pulse modulation, the pulse modulated wave is represented by $u(t) = m(t) g(t)$. The Fourier series of Eq. 11-1 can represent a general periodic waveform. For a train of rectangular pulses of height, h, and width, t, with the origin of time at the midpoint of a pulse

$$g_n = \frac{\omega_0}{\pi} \ t \frac{-}{2} t_2 \ h \cos n\omega_0 t \ dt = \frac{2h}{n\pi} \ \sin \frac{n\omega_0 t}{2} \qquad (11\text{-}2)$$

As t goes to zero

$$g_n \to \frac{2h}{n\pi} \ \frac{\omega_n 0 t}{2} \ = \ 2h f_0 t$$

and $u(t) \to m_1 h f_0 t (\cos \omega_1 t + \cos(\omega_0 + \omega_1)t + \cos(\omega_0 - \omega_1)t$
$+ \cos(2\omega_0 + \omega_1)t + \cos(2\omega_0 - \omega_1)t + \ldots \ldots \quad (11\text{-}4)$

The case of instantaneous sampling is represented by Eq. 11-4, which shows that a band-limited signal can be reproduced from regularly spaced samples taken at a rate exceeding twice the highest signal frequency.

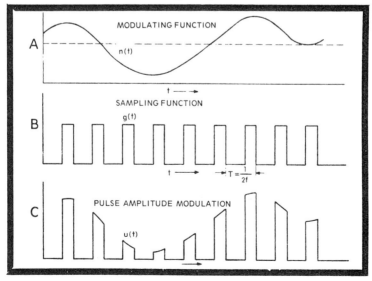

A — MODULATING FUNCTION $n(t)$
$t \longrightarrow$

B — SAMPLING FUNCTION $g(t)$
$t \longrightarrow$ $T = \frac{1}{2f}$

C — PULSE AMPLITUDE MODULATION $u(t)$

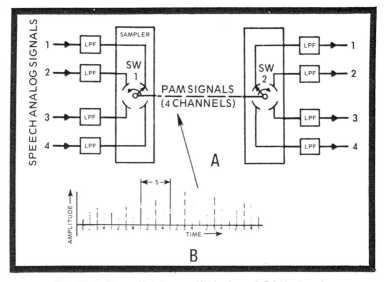

Fig. 11-3. Time-division multiplexing of PAM signals.

TIME-DIVISION MULTIPLEXING

After sampling, independent signals can be assigned mutually exclusive time slots and, if the pulses occupying these slots do not overlap each other in time, a multiplexed signal may be formed. If instead of using the single-channel circuit of Fig. 11-1, a very basic circuit is arranged as shown in Fig. 11-3A, it is possible to multiplex several channels together. In this example only 4 channels are shown, but the same general principles can be applied to 24 or 32 channels. Of course, in practice the rotating switches No. 1 and No. 2 would be replaced by the necessary electronic switches with sufficient speed to provide the sampling rates required. If in this example the maximum message-signal frequency is 4000 Hz, 4 separate channels may be sampled 8000 times per second and 4 separate pulse-modulated signals will be transmitted with their pulse streams interleaved as shown in Fig. 11-3B.

It should be recognized that the sampling frequency is not related to the number of channels to be sampled and transmitted. There is no fundamental limitation to the number of channels that may be assembled in this way. However, there are practical limitations in their transmission. The greater the number of channels examined in this way within each sampling period, the narrower each pulse must be, resulting in a greater required transmission bandwidth to prevent pulse distortion.

Mathematically, the TDM spectrum with all of its interleaved channels can be represented by

$$u(t) = \sum_{n=1} u_n(t) \, g_n(t)$$

for an n-channel system, where $g_n(t)$ is the conductance function of the switching process for the nth channel.

PULSE-CODE MODULATION (PCM)

In principle, PAM signals contain all of the information in the original message. Generally the original message amplitudes occupy a continuous range and so will the sample amplitudes occupy a continuous range of possible values. By a process called **quantization** it is possible to approximate this infinite number of signal amplitudes by a finite number of discrete values in an encoding operation. Briefly, the signal range is divided into a number of smaller ranges with a discrete number assigned to each minor range. In essence, such an operation is like rounding off a number to a fixed number of decimal points. It is inherent in such a process that there will be some loss of information, but such a loss can be kept negligibly small by the use of a sufficient number of minor ranges or steps.

Amplitude Quantization

The sine-wave signal shown in Fig. 11-4A might appear as shown in Fig. 11-4B after being subjected to amplitude quantization. This operation is not done without some sacrifice, in that quantization noise, as shown in Fig. 11-4C, is introduced. This noise inposes some limitations of PCM systems, which will be discussed later. However, its presence makes time-division switching in the PCM mode more desirable than ever.

Given an amplitude-quantized PAM signal with a finite number of amplitude levels, it is possible to allocate to each such level a unique binary code. Each PAM pulse may be replaced by a group of binary pulses, which will identify the amplitude of the PAM pulse which has been replaced. An n-digit binary code enables 2^n quantizing levels to be encoded. Thus, 128 levels will require 7 digits. The results of a simple encoding of a portion of a signal waveform into a 3-digit code

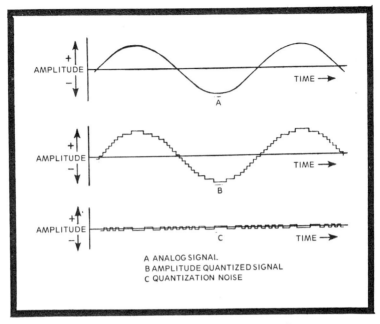

A ANALOG SIGNAL.
B AMPLITUDE QUANTIZED SIGNAL
C QUANTIZATION NOISE

Fig. 11-4. The effects of amplitude quantization.

to produce a PCM signal is shown in Fig. 11-5. After PAM signals have been coded to produce PCM, the signals of separate channels may be interleaved to form a multiplex of channels in a similar manner to that employed with uncoded PAM signals as described previously. Although a PCM signal requires a pulse rate n times as great as an uncoded PAM signal and consequently requires a transmission bandwidth n times as great as the PAM signal, this disadvantage is offset by enough advantages to make its use desirable for certain applications.

Advantages of PCM

The use of PCM signals in TDM transmission systems results in freedom from attenuation and phase distortions, from crosstalk and transmission channel noise, and from variations in the transmitted level due to attenuation in the transmission path. These advantages accrue mainly from the fact that regeneration of the signals is possible at determined points in the transmission path. The regenerated pulses carry no information about the noise or distortion on the preceding link. The proper application of regeneration makes the PCM signals practically independent of the total transmission path, which is in marked contrast to most other forms of transmission, where noise and distortion are cumulative. Thus, the signal-to-noise ratio in a properly designed PCM system is decided by the designer, who chooses the proper points for regeneration of the signals.

Disadvantage of PCM

A major disadvantage in PCM transmission lies in quantizing noise and severe distortion of very low-level signals. For each code-decode operation (necessary with analog message signals) the quantizing noise is cumulative, so coding and decoding should be permitted only once per connection. Thys, once the message has been converted to digital form it should remain in that form over the whole transmission path until its final destination. Therefore, the switching of PCM channels in multiplex form is necessary to realize acceptable levels of quantizing noise and distortion as well as for economic reasons. Although companding can be used to reduce the effects of quantizing noise, it is not sufficient to alter the basic situation just mentioned. Companding

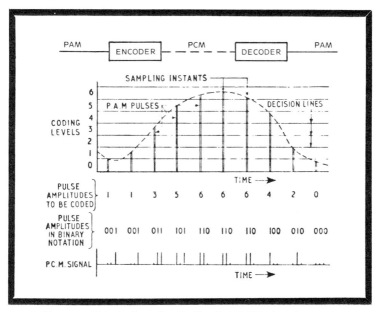

Fig. 11-5. Production of 3-digit-coded PCM signal.

involves compression of the PAM samples by passing them through a nonlinear amplifier, encoding the compressed samples and, after transmission, expanding the signals to their former amplitude range. This operation results in smaller quantum steps being assigned to the range where most of the speech samples are concentrated and larger steps being assigned to the remaining range. This procedure takes advantage of the frequency-volume distribution of the speech samples to reduce the effects of quantizing noise.

PCM SWITCHING PRINCIPLES

In relation to PCM transmission, the advantages of PCM switches is that they are digital and they pass multiplexed signals. A multiplex highway (the common path over which many separate channels can pass with separation achieved by time division) carries the samples of the many channels arranged in time sequence. The two modes of switching, which may be used separately or in combination, are time switching and space switching.

Basically, time switching involves the rearrangement of the channel sequence in the multiplex frame so that the signal in channel A of the input highway is transferred to channel B of the output highway. This is accomplished by storing the appropriate digits into a memory at time slot A and reading them out at the next occurrence of time slot B. Space switching (in the PCM application) involves the interconnection of several multiplex highways by electronic switches acting instantaneously or with a small fixed delay. Thus a signal in channel A of highway X can be connected into the same channel A of some other highway Y. In practice, there are several input highways, such as X1, X2 ..Xm, and several output highways, such as Y1, Y2...Yn, interconnected by an m-by-n matrix of switches. Since the electronic switches can be reset in an interdigital interval, the interconnection patterns in each time slot are independent.

Time Switching

The above description of time switching implies the need for time-slot alignment. However, the need for this can be eliminated by using two memories in the time switch. One memory is used to store the incoming signals on a row-by-row basis and the second memory is used to, in effect, present the proper time slot to the signal. The first is known as the **speech memory** and the second as the **time-switching memory.** As shown in Fig. 11-6, these memories are preceded by a retiming circuit, whose purpose is to control the timing deviations suffered by a signal that has been timed by a synchronizing clock located at some distance from the time-switching point. Such deviations are known as **wander** and **jitter.** The latter is eliminated by rephasing, while slight differences in frequency between the clocks of the two exchanges are compensated by either dropping one binary word (if the local clock is too slow) or leaving one row in the speech memory blank (if the local clock is too fast). This may sound like a significant mutilation of the message, but for clock discrepancies of 10^7 to 10^8, mutilations per channel will range from 1 every 16 minutes to 1 every 2 hours and 40 minutes. Another step in the retiming operation involves utilization of a synchronization code to synchronize the channel timing against a local counter.

Since each point on a PCM switch can be time shared by several ongoing message signals, fewer switch points are required than with an analog space-division switch. In a simple comparison, shown in Fig. 11-7, it is seen that only 12 crosspoints are required in a time-division switch while 32 crosspoints are required in an analog space-division switch to connect the same number of circuits. By an operation known as **supermultiplexing** it is possible to obtain a further economy

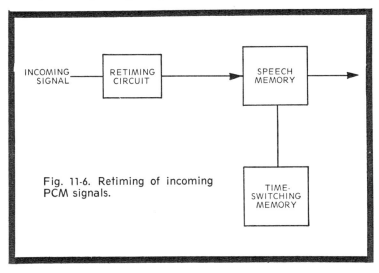

Fig. 11-6. Retiming of incoming PCM signals.

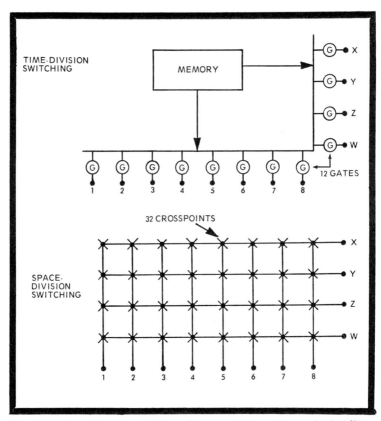

Fig. 11-7. Simplified comparison of crosspoint requirements for time-division and space-division switching.

in crosspoints in a PCM switching system. As shown in Fig. 11-8, supermultiplexing converts the serial bits of a channel into parallel bits. Each PCM line is fed into a shift register and as a typical 8-bit signal is accumulated in the register, it is read out on eight parallel leads, gated through the group multiplexer and presented to the PCM switch matrix in one pulse period. By the serial-to-parallel conversion, supermultiplexing of eight PCM lines onto eight parallel lines is achieved with each channel occupying only one pulse period. The time-switched point now switches eight parallel leads, as opposed to one lead for the serial channel. Thus, it is now an 8-level switch with only one-eighth the total number of gates. Without super-multiplexing, in a typical example, the connection of 96 incoming PCM lines to 96 outgoing PCM lines could require 96 x

96, or 9216 single-level time-switched points. With super-multiplexing of 8 PCM lines together, only 12 x 12 multilevel timed switch points would be required to perform the same operation.

Space and Space-Time Switching

It should be made clear that space switching of PCM signals is not the same as space-division switching of analog message signals. The purpose of PCM space switching is to provide for interconnection between channels of different multiplex highways. Diode gates associated in a matrix may perform this switching by operating at the proper time, as controlled by a space-switching memory associated with the proper highway.

Although PCM time and PCM space switching may be used alone, more compact and economical combinations of the two methods are possible. Sequences range from space-time-space to time-space-time to time-space, with the time usually being considered as a link which interconnects the effectively separate matrices of the PCM space switch. To perform switching in the time switch described above, a speech or **buffer memory** is required at each carrier port plus another memory to control the reading of the first memory. However, since all channels are not busy at any one time, memory words

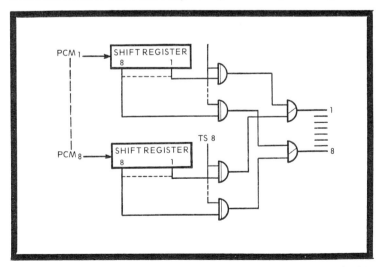

Fig. 11-8. Arrangement for supermultiplexing (GTE Automatic Electric Labs, Inc.).

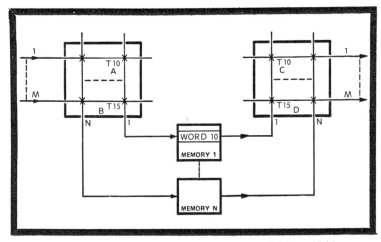

Fig. 11-9. Configuration for space-time-space TDM switching.

that are assigned to idle channels are in excess of requirements. One way to conserve memory words is to locate the time-switch memories between two space switches, where only sufficient storage will be required to handle peak traffic, as shown in Fig. 11-9. To establish a connection, a memory is found that is idle during both the incoming channel time and the outgoing channel time. Let us suppose that we wish to connect channel 10 of port 1 to channel 15 of port m in 24 channel systems. If memory 1 was selected, when channel time C_{10} occurs, both time-switched points A and C are enabled. Memory word 10 is read and gated through time-switched point C. Information from C_{10} is gated through time-switched point A and at the end of the channel time is written into word position 10 of memory 1. When channel time C_{15} occurs, time-switched points B and D are enabled. Memory word 10 is read and the information orginally received from C_{10} is gated through time-switched point D. This word is now available to be outpulsed from the switch in channel 15 to PCM carrier M. Memory word 10 is available to receive $C_{15}m$ information as it propagates through time-switched point B. It is read into memory word 10 at the end of channel time 15 and is held until channel time 10 occurs again.

APPLICATIONS OF PCM SWITCHING

It may be that if the world's communications network be rebuilt PCM time-division switching systems would be chosen to handle all switching operations, especially since data communications is expanding and modern subscriber instruments could be designed to work with PCM transmission and switching systems. However, since any switching system introduced in today's world of communications reality must coexist with a variety of electromechanical and electronic space-division switching systems, the introduction of time-division PCM exchange switching cannot be made without regard for this environment. For a variety of reasons, some of which have already been discussed. PCM switching has not been adopted for local central-office switching. However, there are clear indications that it will play an increasingly important role in tandem and toll exchanges. In England, where time-division switching was pioneered for all exchange applications, successful field trials have been conducted with tandem PCM exchanges. In the U.S., development is being completed on a large new toll PCM exchange, designated No. 4 ESS. In both countries the need for digital exchange switching is being accelerated by the increasing expansion of PCM transmission systems. In the U.S. the rapid growth of Bell's T-1 and T-2 transmission systems has accentuated the need for compatible switching systems, especially at the toll level.

PCM TOLL EXCHANGE (NO. 4 ESS)

To keep pace with the growth of digital transmission systems the Bell Laboratories has developed a new large toll electronic switching system employing time-division techniques. The system uses a solid-state TDM switching network controlled by a stored-program processor, which is also a newly developed equipment. The system has been developed with an analog transmission interface, which allows it to fit directly in place of a No. 4 ETS crossbar system. Having full compatibility with digital transmission systems, it is capable of switching the digital bit stream from transmission lines used in the T-1 and T-2 transmission systems. Analog-to-digital and digital-to-analog converters are required when the network is used with all analog trunks. However, this conversion provides economic advantages over the present systems. As digital carrier transmission in-

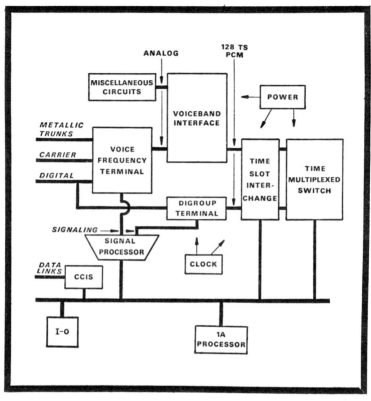

Fig. 11-10. Block diagram of No. 4 ESS system (IEEE-ISS Record).

creases, the direct switching of digital signals will bring economic advantages, because the carrier-channel banks and the converters will be replaced by digital terminals.

The capacity of this exchange is 107,000 terminations of trunks and service circuits. Traffic capability is 1.7 million CCS (peak) at 0.005 blocking, and 350,000 call attempts per hour can be handled. As shown in Fig. 11-10, the system consists basically of a digital network controlled by a stored-program processor aided by a group of signal processors. At the right, various types of transmission channels, both analog and digital, are connected to voice-terminal units. The 4-wire analog outputs of these are connected to a voiceband interface unit, which samples, multiplexes, and encodes analog signals in one direction; and decodes, demultiplexes, and converts digital signals in the other direction. The output of the voice interface unit is a 128-time-slot digital bus carrying 8-bit PCM

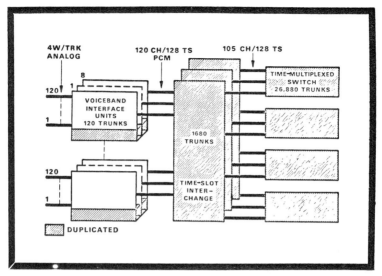

Fig. 11-11. Time-division network of No. 4 ESS (IEEE-ISS Record).

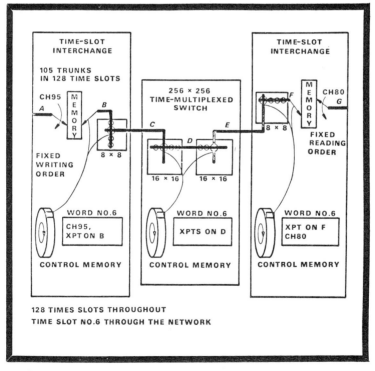

Fig. 11-12. The control memories in No. 4 ESS. (IEE-ISS Record).

signals which are compatible with the D-2 channel banks of the present digital transmission systems. One bus, carrying the output from the coder, and the other bus, carrying the input to the decoder, are connected to the time-slot interchange unit, which provides a stage of switching between time slots on the bus as well as other functions. Its output goes to the time-multiplexed switch, which permits switching of a particular time slot from any bus to one of many others. The output of the time-multiplexed switch goes to the time-slot interchange unit, where digits may be interchanged to another time slot and sent back to the voice interchange unit where they are reconverted to a space-divided analog signal.

Figure 11-11 shows the principal blocks of the switching network, where 120 analog 4-wire channels are connected to the voiceband interface unit. One side of each channel is sampled, multiplexed, and converted to an 8-bit PCM code and sent on a 128-time-slot bus to the time-slot interchange. At the time-slot interchange the trunks on the 7 buses are redistributed equally over 8 buses, each with 105 trunks. Thus, there is an expansion here from 105 to 128 trunks. Each of the time slots occupied by the trunks on any bus may be interchanged onto any other of the 128 time slots on the same bus. This expansion makes a low blocking characteristic possible. After the time-slot interchange operation, the 8 buses are connected to an 8x8 time-divided, time-shared switch located at the time-slot interchange unit. The 8 buses out of this time-switched stage are connected to the time-multiplex switch, where a time slot on any bus may be switched to the same time slot on any other bus.

Figure 11-12 shows the path from input to output of the digital switching network as affected by the memories, which control the path. On highway A the signals from 105 trunks appear in time slots in ordered sequence. They pass into a 128-word memory (one word for each time slot) where they are held for insertion in some other time slot, for not more than one frame (125 usec). The second control memory carries the address to select the gates which connect buses C to D, and D to E, in the time-multiplexed switch. The control memory on the input part of the time-slot interchange selects the gate to connect E to F and the memory location to which the trunk is to be connected. The ordered readout of the memory finally gets the 8-bit PCM words into the time position on G corresponding to the appropriate channel.

Data and Telex Switching  12

The rapid growth of data communications has been influenced primarily by the increasing need to move information to and from computers. Modern time-shared computers can communicate with many data stations simultaneously. Other forms of data transmission which the telephone and telegraph lines are called upon to handle are: batch data transmission, real-time transmission (as in the case of airline reservation systems), banking and credit data, man-computer conversation with the aid of graphics, data collection systems, and automatic meter reading. The combination of computers and data communication places such new requirements on the systems, which must handle them, that one can refer to them better as **teleprocessing** rather than telecommunications. Teleprocessing started with the airline reservation systems, where the distribution of computer data is not as important as the maintenance of an inventory of seats for the whole system and the ability to access such an inventory rapidly at a number of distant points. Another example is that of the banks, who desired to centralize their accounting and provide access to a central file for all their branches. Basically, there are three reasons for the development of teleprocessing systems: the requirement for centralized files, the need to distribute computer services and the advantage gained by having flexibility in location of the operating staff which utilizes the system.

Initially, both the airline and banking operations can be established on a private basis, which would minimize the need for switching operations. But in both cases, the need to expand beyond private operations soon arises. In the case of the airlines, the need arises to access the facilities of other airlines; and in the case of the banks, certain common data facilities may be shared with other banks. Even though private networks may suffice for many services, the need to

215

provide data communications between urban centers leads to regional and national networks. In the U.S., the Bell System, the independent telephone companies, and specialized data communication networks are involved as carriers of such data.

CHARACTERISTICS OF DATA COMMUNICATIONS

The most applicable model for data communications requirements is the central computer conversing with many simple terminals simultaneously. Differing from telephone communications, a data communications network must be able to interconnect a wide variety of subscribers' equipment. Several different types of computer peripherals may appear as network terminals, and so also can computers functioning in several different ways. Terminal speeds ranging from 100 bits/sec to 10,000 bits/sec are likely to be important. Many terminals in current use are constrained by the available communications services, but many of them have variable speeds. One approach to this situation is to provide a buffer store at the terminal, but this approach is expensive. At present, multiaccess computers usually handle terminals of only one speed or with a small number of fixed speeds. It has been proposed that feedback from the output device be used to permit one simple output program to drive terminals with different characteristics. Of course, such feedback signals would have to be handled by the communications network.

As data technology develops, each multiaccess computer is connected to an increasing number of terminals, making it expensive and difficult to provide separate lines from the computer to the network for each of the terminals. Thus, a need for multiplexed connections between the computer and the terminals arises. But this need cannot necessarily be met in a straightforward manner. One characteristic of a data communications network differing from conventional telephone networks is that the two ends of the communication link are very different. One end is a computer capable of flexible behavior, and the other end is a relatively slow terminal with no intelligence. Since the two ends are so different, it would appear that the network would communicate differently with them. The flow of information in a data communication system is intermittent just as it is in the case of telephone conversations. However, instead of minutes of conversation, only a few seconds will elapse for the information flow in one direction, followed by a pause and some flow of information in the opposite direction. The access times for typical computers in use at this time are about 100 msec, but this will become faster as better memories are utilized. The time scale for the interchange of data messages needs to be of this order.

DATA COMMUNICATION METHODS

One approach to communications with the devices mentioned above is to store the digital information at each stage of its progress through the network and retransmit it at the highest possible speed to the following stage. Known as the **store-and-forward**, or **message-switching** system, it is not dissimilar to a system used in telegraph message switching. By using storage along the network path, links of different speeds may be employed and the link to a terminal can operate at a different speed than the link from the computer. When the message unit is a natural unit for communication between processor and processor or terminal and processor, the greatest advantage can be taken of this method.

Circuit Switching

Another approach is to use **circuit switching**, which for digital information would be a time-division multiplexed system. However, a certain minimum amount of message must be transmitted to make the method efficient. If the message is about 1000 bits, it is too short to be sent by circuit switching, and the store-and-forward method offers the better solution. In order to keep messages at this level or lower, it is necessary to break them up into short units called **packets**. Thus, message or store-and-forward systems are often called **packet-switching systems.** If the stored unit can be kept down to 1000 bits, the system delay due to storage can be held to about 10 msec.

It seems that any extensive data network would require both packet and circuit switching, because they perform best with different speeds of traffic—the packet method working best below 1,000 bits and the circuit method working best above 10,000 bits. For intermediate values, it is not clear that one has an advantage over the other, but if the message is broken into packets the store-and-forward method could handle the larger messages. The way in which the two methods may be combined is seen in the multiplex connection between the network and a multiaccess computer. The packet-switching portion of the system will use one or more circuits for such a connection and it will interleave data packets over these circuits. Each packet will carry the address of its destination. The packet sizes will be chosen to accommodate the computer system associated with the network, with breaks between the packets coinciding with pauses in the operation of an input or output mechanism.

Message- and Packet-Switching Networks

The purpose of message or store-and-forward switching is to provide for the handling of record-type communications traffic on a nonreal-time basis. Packet switching is simply a special case in which the message size is controlled to provide the most efficient performance of the system. A message-switching system configuration is shown in Fig. 12-1. The flow of a store-and-forward communication in this system would typically be as follows: a man- or machine-prepared message at a user location is placed on line to be recorded in its respective switching center, X. Permanent records may be made as required and an idle trunk to the terminating center, W, is seized. The message is forwarded to W, where it is recorded and subsequently sent to the addressee when his line is found to be idle. The sequential nature of the operation is indicated by message transmission intervals i_1, i_2, and i_3 in Fig. 12-1. The entire transmission may involve only one-way communication, but not necessarily so. Since an end-to-end connection is not involved, an answer or acknowledgment of receipt of the message will constitute a new message from the former addressee to the addressor. If all trunks are busy between switching centers X and W, alternate routing attempts via centers Y and Z may be made as in the case of circuit switching.

Message Transmission

Such an operation may be controlled by switching-center logic which responds to the addressee, and with routing information in the message. The format of the message usually consists of the following: start of message, message header, text of message, and end of message. The message header would usually contain the address and routing information. An inportant feature of message switching is the ability to arrange outgoing messages in file for any given output channel. This feature is known as **queuing**. Messages may be arranged in the order of their arrival for retransmission, or they may be arranged for preferential treatment according to priority. The latter may be indicated in the message header. Messages are sorted by destination and passed into outgoing line units. In the line units a further sorting may take place to place the messages in stores for high, intermediate, or low-priority transmission. Later they will be fed out of the stores onto the output line in the above order. In a technique related to queuing, **message interpolation** is also possible. In this technique a long message may be interrupted briefly to send a shorter message. For the highest-priority messages, it is possible to design the message center so that the line stores can start retransmission of the message before the full message has been received. This type of operation is the

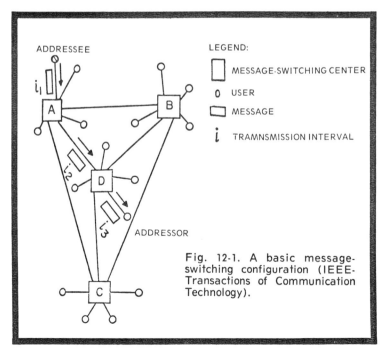

Fig. 12-1. A basic message-switching configuration (IEEE-Transactions of Communication Technology).

closest approach to real-time connections in a message-switching system. If the message is arranged in blocks, the start of registration of a second message block can signal the beginning of the retransmission of the first block. Another feature can provide for preemption of a desired line being used for a lower-priority message in favor of a high-priority message.

With store-and-forward systems it is rather easy to arrange for the multiaddress transmission of messages. Such an arrangement satisfies the requirement for transmitting a message to several users. Generally, this operation would be performed sequentially if there was no need for a real-time result. However, the same message could be sent to several users simultaneously, if it is sent to several message centers so that all of them could transmit at the same time.

Message-switching centers can also provide language and speed conversions. For instance, a teletypewriter might generate Baudot code and a computer might generate an entirely different code. Translation equipment can be provided so that code conversions are made within the message center and both messages could be received at terminations in Baudot code. Translations between various other codes would also be possible, but instructional information relative to routing, priority, and so forth would be required in both languages in each case. Speed conversions are possible by message read-in and registration at one speed, and readout at another predetermined speed on another line or trunk. Such conversion makes user devices of different speeds compatible for intercommunication.

OPERATIONAL MESSAGE-SWITCHING SYSTEMS

One example of a working store-and-forward switching system is the administrative and data network of AT&T's Long Lines Department. It handles administrative traffic, time and payroll reports, circuit-layout records, and plant-service results records through a nationwide network. It uses single and multistation lines for transmitting teletypewriter and data messages. These lines are supervised by an electronic message switcher, which polls the stations, receives their messages, and queues them for delivery to one or more destinations. The switcher is designed around the No. 1 ESS processor, which is supplemented by peripheral units for assembling, storing, and transferring data characters. This system has been designated as No. 1 ESS ADF.

No. 1 ESS ADF

Figure 12-2 shows the relationship between stations, controllers, lines, and the No. 1 ADF. The stations, which may be computer ports or teletypewriters, have individually associated electronic controllers. These respond to polling signals from the No. 1 ESS ADF and register service requests when a customer offers a message for delivery. Although several stations may be on one line, the No. 1 ESS ADF determines which stations receive and deliver a message at any time. As shown in Fig. 12-3, the main elements of the system are (1) an autonomous data-store distributor, (2) buffer control, (3) message store, (4) a tape system, and (5) the central processor. These elements are duplicated for reliability.

Data-Scanner Distributor. The data-scanner distributor employs time-division principles to sample each line at 1650 times a second, and stores the sample taken at the center of each data bit. The memory capability of aluminum-strip ultrasonic delay lines is used in the addressing of lines, the sampling of data being received in serial form from the lines, the storage of each bit in a memory time slot until the entire

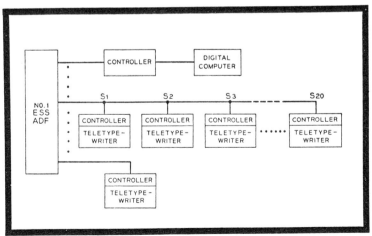

Fig. 12-2. Connection of data terminals to No. 1 ESS APF (Bell Systems Technical Journal).

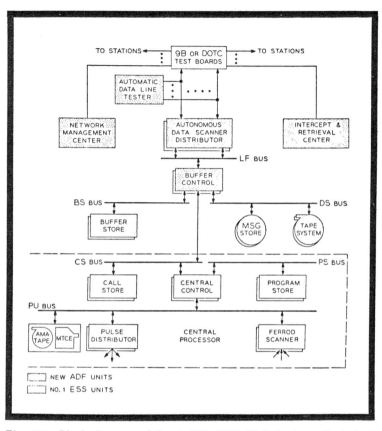

Fig. 12-3. Block diagram of No. 1 ESS ADF (Bell Systems Technical Journal).

data character is received, and the passing of character bits in parallel to the buffer control. There, buffering is provided between the various rates of the peripheral units and the normal cycle time of the central processor. It also relieves the central processor of a large number of repetitive tasks by (1) receiving data characters from the data scanner distributor and assembling these characters into computer words, (2) recognizing and flagging special control characters, (3) performing error-control operations on the data, (4) acting as a buffer in controlling the transfer of messages to and from the message store and the tape system, and (5) interleaving the operation of the data-scanner distributor, message store, tape and central processor subsystems to permit concurrent operation of these asynchronous units.

Message Store. The message store is a sequential-access (block-oriented) memory unit which provides in-transit storage for all messages passing through the system. A disk file, consisting of 4 double-faced rotating disks with a capacity of approximately 60 million bits, provides the storage. The message store retains each originating message until satisfactory delivery has been made to all addresses; stores a cross-reference file consisting of tape search numbers as a function of message numbers for retrieval of messages from the tape system; and stores various types of registers, queues, and data blocks associated with the operational program. Data is stored in fixed record-length blocks on the disk, with each block containing thirty-two 24-bit words, and in a block-interlaced format at approximately 1000 bits $/$ in. The disks are divided into 16 sectors each. Queues are set up in buffer-control call store so that in each revolution 16 blocks of data can be written or read from the disk system. With a disk rotation interval of 40 msec, the average access time for a block of data can be as small as 2.5 msec when a large number of blocks are being handled. The 2 duplicated disk systems provide for 120 million bits of storage with a maximum traffic-handling capacity of approximately 38,400 characters $/$ sec.

The Tape System. The tape system consists of up to 16 tape units per switching center, with 2 tape-unit controls. Each tape-unit control translates the tape instructions received from the buffer control into detailed logic sequences, which are necessary to execute the tape operation. The tape-unit control also assembles, disassembles, and buffers data transferred to and from the tape unit. Tape-unit controls, operating concurrently, work with any tape unit for journal-file, permanent-file, and message-retrieval functions.

Central Processor. The central processor utilizes the central control, call stores, program stores, control circuits, and the maintenance center of standard No. 1 ESS systems. Ferrite-sheet memories are used in the call store and twistors with aluminum cards are used in the program store of the No. 1 ESS ADF.

The No. 1 ESS ADF provides high processing power by concurrent operation of four asynchronous subsystems and the use of wired logic for repetitive functions. Modular growth is available for the addition of high-speed lines and trunks as required for multiple switching-center applications, and economies are effected through the use of available No. 1 ESS equipment.

The ARPA Network

The ARPA (Advanced Research Projects Agency of the U.S. Dept. of Defense) network is a long-distance private data network for interconnecting several multiaccess, time-sharing computer systems. It extends across the U.S. and was planned to serve 18 university centers, but has only been partially activated. It is an example of a working packet-switching network, which can be studied for the possible application of similar methods to comparable situations. The main elements in the ARPA network are the multiaccess computers (called hosts) and the interface message processors (called IMPs). Each host is a multiaccess computer complete with local terminals and peripheral equipment.

The network is formed by the provision of interconnected IMPs, one of which has to be associated in close proximity with each host. The IMPs, connected by 50 kilobit／sec circuits, communicate with each other using data packets of variable length up to 1024 bits. A host communicates with its adjacent IMP via a short high-speed link operating up to 1 megabit sec. The host can dump a complete message of up to 8000 bits into the IMP, with the message being called for on a bit-by-bit basis. A subsequent message would not be called for until the appropriate signals are received. The message-and-packet procedure is shown in Fig. 12-4.

The purpose of the ARPA network is to share files and programs at all hosts connected to the network, which, subject to any barring which may be built into the controlling software, are available at any terminal. In the initial installation terminals could gain access to the network only via a host multiaccess computer; but a new form of IMP can provide for a range of standardized remote-terminal conditions, including connections via modems to leased circuits and the public telephone system. Although the ARPA network covers a large geographical expanse, it serves a relatively small number of terminals and its message handling volume is amall compared to the requirements of a national network. Although the capacities of the interconnecting lines and of the IMPs handling transit traffic would need to be increased by a factor of

100 to 1000 to satisfy the demands of a national commercial network, the ARPA network demonstrates the usefulness and practicability of interconnecting multiaccess computer systems of various types by the use of a packet-switching system.

Store-and-forward message-switching systems are finding their way into an increasing number of private installations throughout the U.S., but have yet to become part of a working national communications network in any country.

Specialized Common Carrier Systems

In the U.S. two independent companies, the Data Transmission Company (Datran) and Microwave Communications, Inc. (MCI), have been established to provide facilities for data transmission outside of the Bell System networks. Both companies will utilize time-division multiplexing in their transmission systems and Datran has indicated that it will employ time-division switching. In so doing, Datran plans to use switching at two levels—in district exchanges and regional exchanges. Subscribers will be connected through a multiplexing arrangement to the nearest district exchange

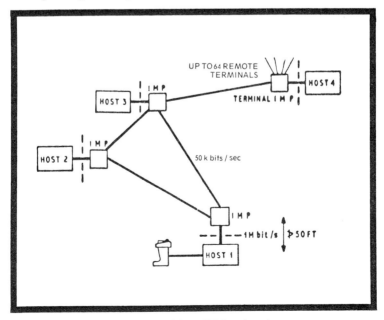

Fig. 12-4. The ARPA network

225

office and the regional exchange will provide network control through the assignment of interoffice trunks. Initially, only 1 switching center will handle the total traffic for all of the 35 cities to be served. However, at the next stage of development the switching functions will expand into 10 district offices and 1 regional office. Finally when the network has expanded to 50 cities, each city will have its own district switching center, and 5 regional switching centers will be established to handle 10 district switching centers each.

Datran plans to take advantage of the high switching speeds of the solid-state gates associated with TDM switching and their compactness, to disperse small switching matrixes throughout the network to serve as concentrators. Each office is to be computer controlled, and the transmission will be primarily by microwave links.

TELEX SWITCHING SYSTEMS

The growth of Telex services has paralleled that of telephone services and probably exceeded it in growth rate. It is now operated in more than 130 countries and has more than 350,000 subscribers. It has grown as an extension to national communications networks and requires a similar routing and numbering plan. The switching equipment, which is in the main electromechanical, is basically similar to that of telephony in present-day installations. However, its information is in digital form, which lends itself to electronic switching techniques. Consequently, one finds a growing use of computer-controlled Telex exchanges and one finds Telex systems considered along with other data communications systems as a part of any proposed national networks. However, it is a very slow-speed data system—operating at 66 words per minute (50 bits/sec) and using the Baudot code. Any teleprinter or teletypewriter on the system in a given country can dial other such devices in that country, and international communications may be had without speed or code conversion.

The Siemens EDS System

A good example of current development in a switching system designed to cater to Telex as well as higher-speed data requirements is the Siemens EDS system. A study of bit-serial and bit-parallel TDM switching methods has led to the provision of different through-connecting techniques for data channels of different speeds. For low-speed Telex subscribers and medium-speed data lines, connections are made to switching groups, which operate bit-serially on the address-code multiplex principle. High-speed data channels and synchronous data networks are served by switching groups which provide for the bit-parallel switching of bit groups. Another possibility that has been considered is to insert space-multiplex switching groups for the through-connection of analog signals or very high bit-rate signals.

Organization of the ESD System

The fact that a wide variety of data speeds were to be accommodated in the most efficient manner has led to a

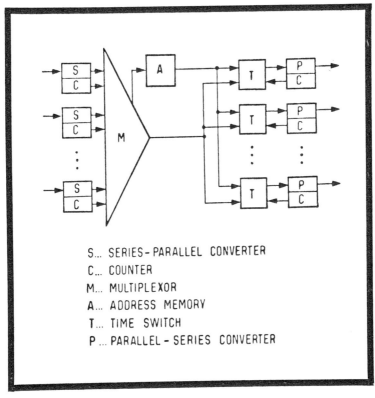

S... SERIES-PARALLEL CONVERTER
C... COUNTER
M... MULTIPLEXOR
A... ADDRESS MEMORY
T... TIME SWITCH
P... PARALLEL-SERIES CONVERTER

Fig. 12-5. Switching unit of EDS for synchronous data networks (IEEE-ISS Records).

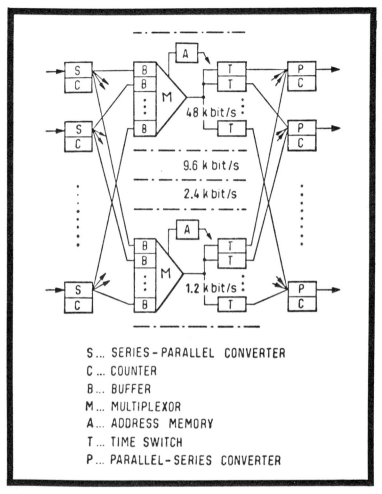

Fig. 12-6. Switching unit of EDS with parallel arrangement (IEEE-ISS Record).

modular design of the EDS system, the structure of which is shown in Figs. 12-5 and 12-6. The need to provide for high-speed data channels and for the employment in synchronous networks, as well as handling low-speed data (such as Telex) has led to the introduction of new features—for example, switching groups utilizing a separate bipolar solid-state memory to relieve the data-traffic load on the basic memory unit, switching groups implementing parallel switching of bit groups for synchronous TDM networks, and switching groups operating on the space-multiplex switching principle.

Automatic Private Branch Exchanges

There are more than 10 million private branch exchange (PBX) and Centrex lines in the U.S. Compared to over 60 million local lines, this a relatively small number. However, these PBX and Centrex lines originate or terminate about 60 percent of all local and long-distance traffic. When in addition it is recognized that about 40 percent of all interoffice trunks are devoted to tie-line service, which permits PBX internal calls to bypass the public network, the full magnitude of PBX operations can be appreciated. It has been estimated that 85 percent of all PBXs serve less than 100 extension lines. However, there are many large-company installations where thousands of extensions are served by PBX equipment. In such cases a large proportion of the exchanges will be capable of serving more than 500 extensions. Although the abbreviation PBX is used to cover either manual or automatic private branch exchanges, it is more common to refer to an **automatic exchange** as a **PABX.**

There are three types of private switching equipment as follows: private branch exchanges (PBXs), community dial offices (CDOs), and key telephone systems. Community dial office equipment is not greatly different from PBX equipment except that it is unattended and without an operator. PBXs as well as PABXs invariably utilize the services of an operator to at least greet the outside caller and exercise a limited amount of control over the system. The basic difference between PBXs and Key Telephone systems is that the former has a high ratio of internal to external traffic, while the latter handles more external traffic than internal traffic. In large-company installations the cost of message units, tolls, and tie-line calls may run as high as 50 percent for the key equipment. In small installations, key equipment may serve the needs of the customer without a PBX, but in large installations where PBX or PABX equipment is required, one will also find key equipment in a support role.

PBX FUNCTIONS

A PBX is in a class above an intercom, because it must provide for external connections with the public telephone network as well as handling a volume of internal traffic between extensions. Connections to the public telephone network are called trunks at the PBX end, but appear the same as individual subscriber lines at the central-office exchange. The number of trunks from the PBX usually ranges from about a tenth to a fourth the number of extensions, but there may be considerable variations due to WATS lines, tie-lines, etc.

Despite the automatic character of most PBXs, many basic functions are performed by the operators. These include answering outside calls to the directory number where the PBX is located; handling of person-to-person, collect and special calls; locating called parties not at their extension by paging; transferring calls; assisting internal users with tie-line or long-distance calls; setting up conference calls, and keeping cost and traffic records. Often the operator is only essential to these functions in special cases, because many of them can be performed automatically. In the most modern PABX equipment the operator is relieved to such an extent that she can function easily as a receptionist or part-time secretary.

In addition to providing for automatic internal calls, incoming calls, and automatic outgoing calls, typical modern PABX equipment can provide many other features. A number of these are listed below.

1. **Camp-on-Busy.** This allows incoming calls to a busy extension to be held until the extension is free.

2. **Call Back and Transfer.** This allows an extension holding conversation with an exchange line to talk to another extension while still holding the first exchange line, and to reconnect to the first exchange line by dialing a prescribed digit.

3. **Night Transfer.** Permits all calls from exchange lines to be received by one or more predetermined extensions. In addition, recall from extensions, and connection changes after transfer are possible.

4. **Number Group.** This allows the change of numbers freely without altering the position of extensions on the switching equipment by adding special equipment.

5. **Restricted Service.** Preventing certain extensions from having direct access to central-office trunks is the purpose of this feature.

6. **Add-on Conference.** Permits the addition of a second extension to an established incoming exchange call.

7. **Call Advance.** Provides for the transfer of an incoming call to another nearby extension when the desired one is busy.

8. **Tie-Line Service.** Allows the connection of tie lines to extensions through an identifying digit without operator assistance.

9. **Registration of Outgoing Calls.** Provides counting of the number of outgoing calls from an extension.

10. **Executive Override and Preemption.** Permits selected extensions to override an existing conversation and gain access by dialing an additional digit after receiving a busy tone. A warning tone is provided to the engaged parties.

11. **Automatic Callback.** Allows the caller, when a busy signal is encountered, to dial a single-digit number and hang up. When the calling and called parties are free, both are rung automatically and the call is completed.

12. **Abbreviated Dialing.** Permits the calling of a predetermined outside subscriber by dialing two or three digits.

PABX SWITCHING SYSTEMS

Most of the basic circuit-switching methods using in central offices have been applied in the design of PABX exchanges, and equipments incorporating them are still in use throughout the world. Initially, progressive systems such as step-by-step and rotary types dominated the scene, but during the past decade, crossbar switching has been applied extensively. Paralleling the development of electronic switching methods for the central-office applications, there has been considerable development of electronic switching systems for PABX applications. Of course, cost has been a factor in the introduction of such designs and only recently has a number of such exchanges appeared on the competitive market. These include space-division systems utilizing reed relays and solid-state crosspoints, as well as time-division systems utilizing PAM switching techniques. All modern designs incorporate common control, and a few of the latest designs feature stored-program control using minicomputer processors.

BELL SYSTEM PABX

The several Bell System PABX equipments, manufactured by the Western Electric Company, are typical of the types available. Four types utilizing crossbar switching and relay common control are as follows:

Model Designation	Maximum Extension Lines
558A	40
756A	60
757A	200
770A	400

In another category, the Bell System has introduced their 800 series with a space-division, ferreed switching network and wired-logic electronic common control in all models except the 805A, which uses crossbar switching with wire-logic, electronic common control. These are as follows:

Model Designation	Maximum Extension Lines
805A	57
800A	80
801A (Heavy traffic)	180
801A (Medium traffic)	270
801A (Light traffic)	270

In a third category there is Bell's 101 ESS, which employs time-division switching of PAM inputs and stored-program control. By a family of switch units it is possible to provide this exchange in various capacities as follows:

Model Designation	Maximum Extension Lines
No. 101 ESS (2A Switch)	364
No. 101 ESS (3A Switch)	820
No. 101 ESS (4A Switch)	4000

Although some of the largest PABX installations today are of the centralized extension (Centrex) type, with central-office equipment like No. 5 crossbar and No. 1 ESS serving as the main part of the operation, step-by-step PABX systems are being offered for some of the largest installations with unlimited line capacity. These include Bell's model 701B and Automatic Electric's type 311.

THE INTERCONNECTION OF PRIVATELY-OWNED PABXS

Prior to 1968 the U.S. telephone companies protected themselves from competition by stipulating in their tariffs that only telephone company equipment could be connected, attached, or made a part of the communications network. However in June, 1968, AT&T was ordered by the FCC to revise its interstate tariffs to allow the interconnection of a device called the Carterfone, which acoustically coupled private mobile-radio systems to the telecommunications network.

These revised tariffs liberalized the prohibition against the interconnection of customer-owned equipment to include electrically connected equipment, and established three major conditions for such interconnection as follows.

1. Customer-provided terminal equipment cannot endanger the safety of telephone company employees or the public; damage or require change in or the alteration of the equipment or other facilities of the telephone company; interfere with the proper function of such equipment or facilities; or impair the operation of the telecommunications system, or otherwise injure the public in its use of the telephone company's services.

2. Connection to the network must be made through a company-provided and -maintained connecting arrangement, and network control signaling must be by telephone company equipment.

3. Customer-provided equipment must meet minimum protection criteria, which limit the power and frequency input to the network.

After the Carterfone decision and the approval of interconnection, studies indicated that there was a substantial market for customer-owned equipment as well for leasing from other companies than Bell or the independent telephone companies. PABX equipment was one of the major categories that the studies showed to have great potential for the future. Concurrently, great interest rose importing PABX equipment. Practically every telephone exchange manufacturer outside of the Communist bloc was offering PABXs to the U.S. interconnection market. Also, at the same time, several U.S. developers and manufacturers not previously in the telephone equipment field undertook the development and sale of new PABX equipment. In 1973 a survey of the available PBX systems showed 111 such systems from 22 manufacturing sources.

TYPICAL PABX SYSTEMS

The predominant switching system found in the greatest number of PABXs is the crossbar type. Reed relays are also used with electronic common control in a few types. The other types that have received most attention utilize either solid-state space-division switching components or time-division switching of PAM signals derived from the analog messages. A few of either of these switching methods combined with stored-program control have also appeared.

The use of either solid-state space-division crosspoints or time-division switching offers appeal to those who may wish to feed data transmissions through the PABX, because of the higher switching speeds. Notable in the PABX type with solid-state crosspoints and stored-program control are the IBM type 2750 and its successor, the 3750—both which are labeled as voice- and data-switching systems. Philco-Ford has also recently introduced its PC 512 with comparable switching techniques. Although the Philco-Ford exchange is smaller than the IBM types, it is available in the U.S. while IBM has offered the PABXs only in the European market. Several time-division PABXs, with or without stored-program control, are becoming available. Of course, the most notable one with stored program control is Bell's No. 101 ESS.

Obviously there are so many PABXs on the U.S. market that an entire book would be required to describe them, so only one or two types in each of the above categories will be covered on the following pages.

Japan's CP 20 Crossbar Exchange

A popular crossbar type of PABX introduced in Japan in 1968, which is typical of the crossbar PABXs in general, is the type CP20. It is a fully common-control type and will work with dial, battery, or magneto systems. It was designed to serve from 70 to 500 extension lines and is suitable for medium-sized offices and factories. The trunking scheme of the CP 20 in both its cord and cordless versions is shown in Fig. 13-1. When the attendant board is the cord type, incoming calls are connected by means of pair cords. With the cordless type, incoming calls are connected through the position link to the attendant board, then connected through the switch frame with the aid of the operator.

The frame composition of the main switching network consists of a combined 2- or 3-stage connection system with an extension-line capacity of 100 per frame. In practice the position link is composed of a part of the tertiary switch (TS) of the switch frame. Dialing speeds of either 10 or 20 pulses∕sec can be accommodated.

The cabinet in which the exchange is housed consists of three frames, each of which is set on a guide-rail rack in a row, so that setting up work is easy. Each frame can be turned around on its axis for ease of inspection. The cabinet is an assembly type, which can be assembled with bolts and nuts on

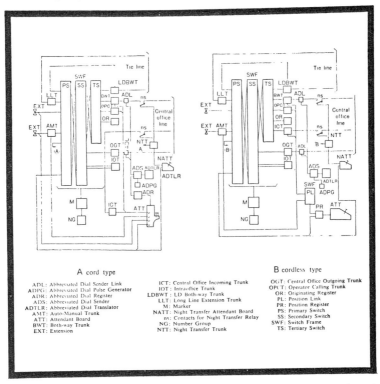

A cord type   B cordless type

ADL: Abbreviated Dial Sender Link
ADPG: Abbreviated Dial Pulse Generator
ADR: Abbreviated Dial Register
ADS: Abbreviated Dial Sender
ADTLR: Abbreviated Dial Translator
AMT: Auto-Manual Trunk
ATT: Attendant Board
BWT: Both-way Trunk
EXT: Extension

ICT: Central Office Incoming Trunk
IOT: Intraoffice Trunk
LDBWT: LD Both-way Trunk
LLT: Long Line Extension Trunk
M: Marker
NATT: Night Transfer Attendant Board
ns: Contacts for Night Transfer Relay
NG: Number Group
NTT: Night Transfer Trunk

OGT: Central Office Outgoing Trunk
OPCT: Operator Calling Trunk
OR: Originating Register
PL: Position Link
PR: Position Register
PS: Primary Switch
SS: Secondary Switch
SWF: Switch Frame
TS: Tertiary Switch

Fig. 13-1. Trunking layout of Japan's CP 20 PABX (Nippon Telegraph and Telephone Public Corp.).

the subscriber's premises. The fully equipped switching system in its cabinet weighs only about 360 pounds.

The cordless attendant board is a pushbutton type, while the cord attendant board is a typical switchboard type. The power source facility consists of a constant-voltage silicon rectifier and a battery box.

With regard to maintenance, it is possible to record trouble status automatically and to test extension lines by means of plug-in connections. Alarms are indicated on the faces of the cabinets and on attendant boards to that remedial action can be taken immediately. Traffic of the trunks and the common-control equipments is recorded by additional counters.

Philco-Ford Model PC 512 (EPABX)

The model PC 512 has a straightforward 4-stage switching network, as shown in Fig. 13-2. Each switch matrix (8x4 and 4x4 crosspoints) is composed of silicon-controlled rectifiers (SCRs). This stored-program-controlled exchange has fully redundant call processor-memory units with automatic switchover. One processor-memory unit is online, with the standby unit being constantly updated to insure control continuity. The stored program provides flexibility for directory changes, call-forward and call-back capabilities, hunt groupings, call splitting, as well as a number of other capabilities, which require only minor program changes. Actually, 39 operational features are listed by the manufacturer. This exchange can handle up to 512 lines and has a crosstalk attenuation of better than 65 dB from 300 to 3200 Hz.

Based on a grade-of-service probability of P.01, the maximum traffic capability of the model PC 512 is 9 CCS∕line at 256 lines and 6 CCS∕line at 512 lines. These values are based on fully equipped concentrator and trunk-link-network stages. The capacity may be reduced by using fewer or partly loaded matrix boards in the concentrator and trunk-link stages, thus tailoring traffic requirements to specific applications at a consequent reduction in cost. Loads of approximately 3.2 or 6.0 CCS—line for up to 256 lines, and 1.86 or 3.2 CCS∕line for switch configurations above 256 lines may be achieved in this manner. Distributed-link-search techniques are used to increase the traffic capability of this exchange and afford maximum usage at the traffic rates mentioned.

In order to provide the most efficient usage of available linkage, the traffic load must be distributed as evenly as possible across the available matrix paths. The use of one or more common-path-selection techniques using random or sequential selection may not produce the optimum link usage. In this exchange the stored-program control permits a more sophisticated path search. Equipment and path usage is stored in memory in a fashion, which makes a comparative analysis of the amount of link group usage relatively easy to perform. When a call is marked through the matrix, it is placed through link groups with the least amount of traffic in

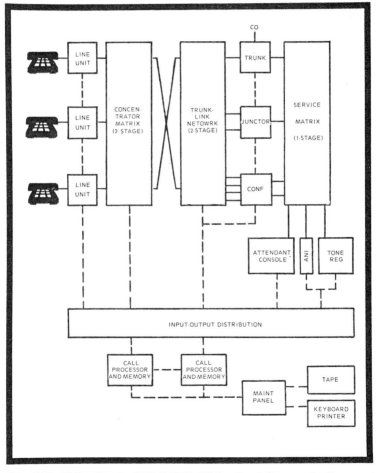

Fig. 13-2. Philco-Ford's SPC PABX (Philco-Ford Communications and Technical Services Div.).

progress. This ordered placing of calls evenly distributes traffic and provides a maximum number of available paths in the switching network.

On command from the printer keyboard, traffic usage data is temporarily stored in memory. Data is acquired in 10 sec scanning intervals and printed in hardcopy form in 15 min cumulative increments. The statistical gathering period may be continued for as long as desired.

Maintenance tests are limited to conventional trunk and station tests at the EPABX terminal, power tests, manipulation of a cassette transport, and operation of a keyboard-printer. Trouble isolation is accomplished by loading-test and diagnostic-program tapes, reading trouble indicators on the printer, and using the keyboard to transmit simple instructions. Replacement of PC boards is made at the direction of the printer, and defective PC boards are returned to the factory for replacement. The maintenance panel is seen in Fig. 13-3 in its relation to the call-processing and control-distribution system of this exchange.

Administrative tasks are accomplished via the keyboard-printer. These include the accumulation of traffic usage data; suspension, connection, and directory-number changes on station lines; and alteration of line-hunting groups.

Northern Electric's EPABX with TDM Switching

A small PABX with 80-line capacity, using TDM switching in the PAM mode, has been developed by Northern Electric of Canada, and is now available in the U.S. Advantage is taken of **resonant transfer**, a technique employed in Bell's No. 101 ESS, to effect an efficient transfer of the sample-pulse energy. With this method, the resonant period of the transmitting and receiving network is made equal to twice the duration of the sampling pulse. During the period when the sampling switch is closed, all of the energy stored on the transmitting side of the resonant circuit flows into the receiving side and is prevented from returning by the opening of the switches.

Transmission over the single TDM highway is effected in a 2-wire unbalanced configuration. The time partitioning is 25 time slots in 1 frame interval, with each time slot 3.33 usec in length. Twenty-four time slots are allocated for calls in progress, and one for scanning. With a frame interval of 83.3

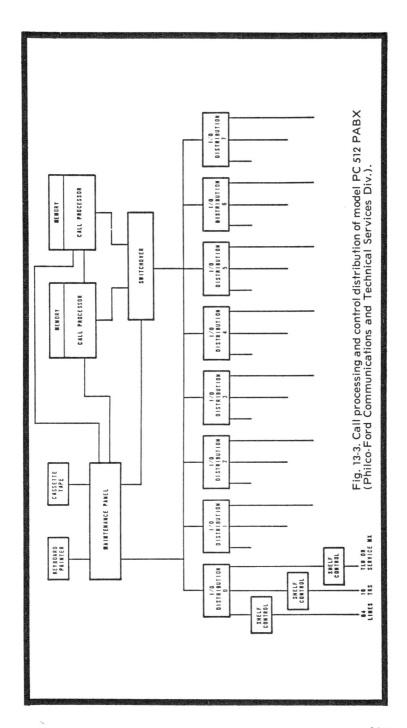

Fig. 13-3. Call processing and control distribution of model PC 512 PABX (Philco-Ford Communications and Technical Services Div.).

(25 x 3.33) usec, 24 simultaneous telephone conversations are accommodated on a single highway. For the 80-line system the switching capacity is 7.9 CCS/line, where 40 percent of all originating calls are intercom. The switching capacity is 30 CCS/line at 20 lines. Approximately half of the time is used for the interconnection of two peripheral circuits (line to line, line to trunk, or line to attendant, etc.) during the 3.33 usec time slot. Crosstalk between adjacent time slots is eliminated by using the remaining time to clamp the highway to ground. A high-transmission-performance quality is realized by the 12 kHz sampling rate of the 83.3 usec period.

One line is scanned by the central control to determine its state (on-hook or off-hook) during time slot number 25 of each frame. Thus, in the maximum-size system the scan rate for lines is one scan per 6.5 msec (80 x 83.3 usec). The worst-case scan rate is approximately 10 msec for detection of request for service, if the scanning requirements for all trunks and lines are included.

The basic equipment unit has a capacity for 40 lines and 15 trunks, but can be expanded to 80 lines and 30 trunks by two additional equipment shelves. Optional service features are plug-in.

Centralized Extension Service (Centrex)

By utilizing switching equipment already installed in central offices or by installing new equipment there rather than installing many local PBX or PABX systems, it is possible to extend service to each extension at office or factory locations so that direct inward dialing (DID) and direct outward dialing (DOD) are possible. Such an arrangement is called **centralized extension service** or Centrex. It has the advantage that no space is required for switching and power equipment on the subscriber's premises, and the switching system can be concentrated where it can be used more effectively, with the effort required for maintenance greatly reduced and flexibility relative to subscriber moves greatly increased. Generally, it has been applied primarily to large industrial or commercial subscribers, but it can be appllied to smaller users as well.

Actually, Centrex service does not require the development of new switching systems for use in the central office. It can be provided by No. 5 crossbar systems or by No. 1 ESS systems, by adaptations, as has been done for some very large installations such as that at the Pentagon, in Washington, D.C. Centrex service is being provided extensively not only in the U.S., but in other countries as well. For example, in Japan the Nippon Telegraph and Telephone Corporation has been installing its C410 crossbar switching system (based on its C400 system described in Chapter 7) especially for Centrex service. In Fig. 13-4 the general trunking scheme of the C410 system is shown, with shaded areas indicating the equipment that had to be added for Centrex.

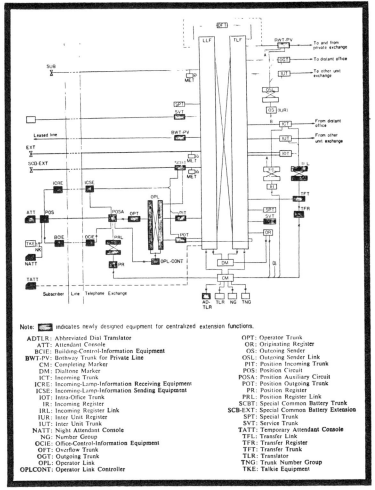

Note: ▨ indicates newly designed equipment for centralized extension functions.

ADTLR: Abbreviated Dial Translator
ATT: Attendant Console
BCIE: Building-Control-Information Equipment
BWT-PV: Bothway Trunk for Private Line
CM: Completing Marker
DM: Dialtone Marker
ICT: Incoming Trunk
ICRE: Incoming-Lamp-Information Receiving Equipment
ICSE: Incoming-Lamp-Information Sending Equipment
IOT: Intra-Office Trunk
IR: Incoming Register
IRL: Incoming Register Link
IUR: Inter Unit Register
IUT: Inter Unit Trunk
NATT: Night Attendant Console
NG: Number Group
OCIE: Office-Control-Information Equipment
OFT: Overflow Trunk
OGT: Outgoing Trunk
OPL: Operator Link
OPLCONT: Operator Link Controller

OPT: Operator Trunk
OR: Originating Register
OS: Outgoing Sender
OSL: Outgoing Sender Link
PIT: Position Incoming Trunk
POS: Position Circuit
POSA: Position Auxiliary Circuit
POT: Position Outgoing Trunk
PR: Position Register
PRL: Position Register Link
SCBT: Special Common Battery Trunk
SCB-EXT: Special Common Battery Extension
SPT: Special Trunk
SVT: Service Trunk
TATT: Temporary Attendant Console
TFL: Transfer Link
TFR: Transfer Register
TFT: Transfer Trunk
TLR: Translator
TNG: Trunk Number Group
TKE: Talkie Equipment

Fig. 13-4. Trunking scheme of Japan's C410 crossbar system supplying Centrex service (Nippon Telegraph and Telephone Public Corp.).

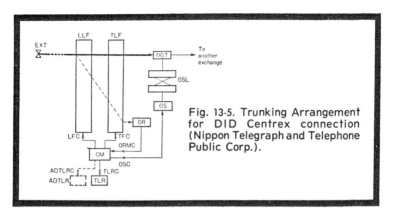

Fig. 13-5. Trunking Arrangement for DID Centrex connection (Nippon Telegraph and Telephone Public Corp.).

The following connections are provided: direct outward dialing from an extension to the outside, direct inward dialing to an extension, internal connection between extensions within the subscriber group, incoming connection through the attendant's console, originating connection through the attendant's console, through-attendant transfer, and busy-line call-forwarding. The steps involved in making the first two of these connections, DOD and DID, will be described here.

DOD Connection from an Extension to the Outside

When an extension user lifts his handset, a dial-tone marker (DM) is activated in the line-link frame (LLF), and a line-marker connector (LMC). Dial-tone marker DM selects an idle originating registor (OR) and connects the calling extension line to OR through LLF and the trunk-link frame (TLF). (See Fig. 13-5). Then an internal dial tone of 400 Hz intermitted 120 times per minute is sent back from OR to the calling extension. When the caller dials 0, the dial tone is changed into a continuous tone.

There are two kinds of originating registers in this system: OR for receiving dial pulses, and OR for receiving pushbutton dialing. Register OR can receive and store a maximum of nine digits exclusive of prefix number in conformity with Japan's nationwide numbering plan.

When the caller finishes dialing, OR activates a completing marker (CM) and sends information to CM regarding the called subscriber's number, etc. Marker CM activates an idle translator (TLR) and TLR translates the information sent from CM into the information used by CM for selecting a

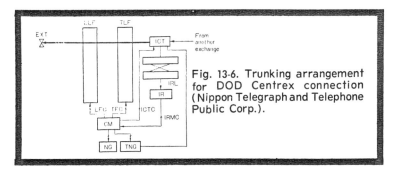

Fig. 13-6. Trunking arrangement for DOD Centrex connection (Nippon Telegraph and Telephone Public Corp.).

desired outgoing trunk (OGT) and restricting certain connections—that is, toll originating connections—to the outside. Marker CM selects an idle OGT belonging to a route indicated by TLR. Then CM establishes connection between the calling extension and the selected OGT over the main switching network. On the other hand, upon selection of the OGT, CM selects an idle originating sender (OS), and makes a connection between OS and OGT through the OS link (OSL). Originating sender OS receives the numbers to be sent to the destination from CM. There are two kinds of originating senders according to the type of signal to be sent: dial-pulse OS and multifrequency OS. Finally, OS sends the called number to the destination.

Direct Inward Dialing (DID) to an Extension

This is an automatic connection from the outside to an extension. First, an incoming trunk (ICT) is activated from the outside and ICT selects, through an incoming register link (IRL), either an idle DP incoming register (DPIR) or MFIR, according to the signal type adopted for the incoming trunk. After receiving the called extension's DID number from the calling exchange, IR engages an idle CM to which IR transmits the number. Completing marker CM begins operation by activating the trunk number group (TNG) to secure information as to ICT's location on TLF and the kind of service. Then CM seizes the number group (NG) and determines the called extensions's location on LLF. A hunting operation proceeds in NG when a hunting group number is received. In preparation for a possible transfer, the subscriber group number of the called extension is transmitted from CM to the ICT and stored there. The CM ends its operation by establishing the speech path between ICT and the called extension over the main switching network.

Glossary

access

The existence of paths within a network from an input terminal to a set of output terminals in the absence of traffic is indicated by the term **access**. Full access permits connecting to all output terminals by unique paths; multiple access indicates that all output terminals can be reached in more than one way; partial access refers to the ability to reach only a fraction of the output terminals.

accessibility (availability)

The number of trunks of the required route in a switching network which can be reached from an inlet.

adaptor

A device designed to switch a number of voice-frequency telephone channels coming from a non-time-division switching system to a time-division multiplex highway.

alternate routing

A procedure by which several routes are searched to complete a connection. The various routes involve different switching stages or switching networks. Usually the route having the fewest switching stages is tested first.

analog transmission

The transmission of continuously variable signals rather than discretely variable signals. Prior to the use of digital encoding and PCM, it was the only way of transmitting voice signals over telephone channels.

area code

A 3-digit prefix dialed ahead of the normal 7-digit telephone number to permit direct distance dialing.

asynchronous system

A system in which the transmission of each information character is individually synchronized usually by the use of start and stop elements.

average holding time

The average duration of a call expressed in seconds or minutes.

bit

The smallest binary unit of information. A contraction of the words **binary digit**.

bit rate

The rate or speed at which bits are transmitted. Bits per second is a common measure.

blocking (congestion)

A condition where the immediate establishment of a new connection is impossible due to the lack of available paths, or the inability to interconnect two idle network terminals because some of the applicable links between them are used for other connections.

Boolean algebra

A form of nonquantitative algebra for dealing with logic functions, originally expressed by British mathematician George Boole (1815-1864).

Broadband exchange (BEX)

Public switched communication system featuring full duplex (FDX) connections of various band-widths. A Western Union facility.

busy hour

An uninterrupted period of 60 minutes in which the total traffic of a sample is a maximum.

byte

A unit of information in electronic computer terminology consisting of 8 bits, referred to as extended binary coded decimal information of an EBCDIC code.

call congestion ratio

The ratio of the time during which congestion exists to the total time considered. It is an estimate of the probability that an external observer will find a system in a congested condition.

calling rate

Average calls per subscriber per hour.

call store

The memory section of a stored program control switching system in which temporary information used in the processing of calls through the exchange is contained. It is also referred to as the Process Store.

central office

Exchanges where subscriber lines and private branch exchange lines terminate. There they are switched to provide the desired connection with other subscribers. Such an exchange is called an end office and is designated as a Class 5 office in the U.S.

central processor

The main computer element of a stored program control switching system, which under the direction of the stored program establishes switching network connections and also monitors and analyzes the system to insure proper operation. Routine process testing, maintenance and administrative functions are also carried out.

Centrex

A PABX system in which the switching equipment is located centrally and away from the location being served. Direct inward dialing (DID) and direct outward dialing (DOD) as well as automatic number identification (ANI) are provided by such a system.

characters

The elements of a message. One computer character consists of 8 bits or 1 byte and is known as an EBCDIC character.

circuit switching

Telecommunications switching in which the incoming and outgoing lines are connected by a physical path, as through crosspoints or switch contacts.

class of service

The services and facilities offered to each individual terminal connected to a system. This information is usually stored with the directory or equipment numbers of the associated terminal, and is accessed by the call processors when a connection is required to or from that terminal.

clock

Equipment to provide a time base for a switching system. In time-division switching it is used to control sampling rates, duration of signal digits, etc.

codec

The combination of a coder and decoder, as used in time-division switching systems to code the incoming message and decode the message being returned to the caller. It is a contraction of the words **coder** and **decoder.**

common control

An exchange control method in which the dialed signals are received and registered separately from the switching elements before they are used to control these switches. Also defined as a control method, which identifies the input and output terminals of the switching network and then causes a connecting path to be established between them. Such systems are also designated as marker systems.

concentration stage

A switching stage in which a number of input lines are connected to a smaller number of output lines or trunks, as in the connection of a large number of subscriber lines to a smaller number of trunks based on the grade of service desired.

congestion function

Any function used to relate the degree of congestion to the traffic intensity.

connecting row

> All those crosspoints directly accessible from an inlet. Only one connection can be established via a connecting row at any instant.

connecting stage

> A connection in a homogeneous switching network uses a number of crosspoints in series. If the crosspoints included in a connection are numbered starting with the closest to the network inlets, then all connecting matrices containing crosspoints that are used as nth crosspoints in such connections are said to belong to the nth connecting stage.

crossbar switch

> A switch having a plurality of vertical paths, a plurality of horizontal paths and electromagnetically operated mechanical means for connecting any of the vertical paths with the horizontal paths.

crosspoint

> A crosspoint comprises a set of contacts that operates together and extends the speech and signal wires of the desired connection. Each connection in a space-division switching network is established by closing one or more crosspoints.

crosstalk

> An unwanted transfer of signals from one circuit to another as may occur between switching elements or circuit wiring.

day to busy hour ratio

> The ratio of the 24 hour day traffic volume to the busy hour traffic volume. In some countries the reciprocal of this ratio is used.

delay system

> A switching system in which a call attempt, which occurs when all accessible paths for the required connection are busy, is permitted to wait until a path becomes available.

dial pulse

> The signaling pulse which is formed by the interruption of the current in the DC loop of a calling telephone. Such interruptions are produced by the breaking of the dial pulse contacts of the calling telephone subset during the dialing process.

Dimond ring translator

> An array of ring-type induction coils associated with coded wiring in such a manner that the translation of directory numbers to equipment number or vice versa can be accomplished in an exchange. It is named after its originator, T. L. Dimond of the Bell Telephone Laboratories.

direct control

> An exchange control method in which pulses, dialed by the subscribers, control directly the route selection switches of the system. For each digit dialed the equivalent of one set of selector switches is required with this control method.

director

> A control element which provides a measure of common control in step-by-step or Strowger exchanges.

distributing frame

> A structure for terminating the wires of a telephone exchange in such a manner that cross-connections can be made readily. Examples are the Main Distribution Frame (MDF) at the entry of an ex-

change, Intermediate Distribution Frames (IDF) between sections of an exchange, and Power Distribution Frames (PDF).

distribution stage

A switching stage between a concentration stage and expansion stage, which has the same number of inlets and outlets and serves as a means of selecting trunks to the desired terminations.

DUV

Data Under Voice. (AT&T System)

electromechanical switching system

An exchange system in which both the speech paths and the control equipment are switched by electromechanical components—such as relays, rotary switches, etc.

electronic switching system

An exchange system in which at least the control equipment is composed of electronic circuits and components, generally of a solid-state type.

EMD switch

The speech-path switching element used in a Siemens rotary switching system. EMD is an abbreviation of Edelmetall-Motor-Drehwahler, which translates in English to Noble-Metal Motor Switch.

end office

A central office or Class 5 office.

entraide

A switching system in which outlets from a given connecting stage are connected to inlets of the same or a previous stage. In such systems calls may traverse a stage more than once. Usually these reentering links are used as last choice paths and the resulting network is heterogeneous. Such an arrangement is used in ITT's Pentaconta Crossbar system.

erlang

The unit of traffic intensity, which is measured in call-seconds per second or call-minutes per minute. Also, one erlang equals 3600 call-seconds per hour. It is named after A. K. Erlang, the Danish engineer and mathematician who first adopted it.

expansion stage

A switching stage which gives access to a larger number of subscriber or output lines from a smaller number of trunk or input lines ahead of it.

extended area service (EAS)

Service which extends the subscriber's access to lines beyond his local exchange as in the case of Direct Distance Dialing.

ferreed

A combination of reed contacts and remanent magnetic members used to provide crosspoints in the switching networks of No. 1 and No. 2 ESS systems.

four-wire circuit

A circuit which uses separate pairs of conductors for outgoing and incoming calls. One pair is for the outgoing channel and the other pair is for the return channel.

frame (equipment)

A structure containing one section of the equipment in an exchange.

frame (time-division multiplex)

A frame comprises the binary speech digits and signaling bits resulting from a single sample of each channel of the total multiplex and any additional distinctive synchronizing signal. A multiframe results from the submultiplexing of one of the speech channels (or the synchronizing channel) to a lower speed facility. A superframe is the assembly of digits formed by combining a frame of each group of a PCM supergroup.

grade of service

Although often defined as the ratio of the number of lost calls to the number of calls attempted, it is also defined in terms of the probability of finding all of the circuits engaged and as any practical interpretation of a congestion function.

grading (graded multiple)

Grading is obtained by the partial multipling of the outlets of connecting networks when each network provides only limited availability to the outgoing group of trunks. There are several types of grading—such as, homogeneous grading, transposed multiple, progressive and O'Dell grading.

grid

A combination of two or more stages of switch blocks connected together to accommodate numbers of input and output circuits as needed to meet the speech-path switching requirements of a given exchange design.

group (supergroup)

In time-division multiplexing, a group can consist of the number of channels handled in one TDM multiplex—such as, a 24 voice-channel combination. By a similar definition, a supergroup consists of a combination of groups as mentioned here.

highway

A common path over which by time division a number of separate channels can pass with adequate separation.

holding time

The total duration of one occupation of a communication channel. The setting-up of a call, conversation, etc. are all classes of holding time.

hunting

A method of concentrating traffic in which one switch is required per line, as in the case of the line-switch method which has been used in step-by-step systems.

interface

The apparatus required to interconnect two equipments having different functions. The type and form of the signals to be interchanged via those circuits must be taken into account.

interconnecting number

A number of grading groups connected together in a homogeneous grading, which is a form of grading in which the outlets of an identical number of grading groups are connected to each outgoing trunk.

interconnecting number (mean)

The quotient obtained by dividing the total number of outlets in a grading by the number of trunks serving the grading.

interconnection

A term applied to the connection of telephone apparatus and equipment, not furnished by the common carriers, to the telephone system serving a given area.

jitter

A variation with a very short time constant affecting the discrepancies between two nominally synchronous timing sources.

junctor

Any link between the central stages of a switching network—such as, between the line-link frame and the trunk-link frame.

line finder

A two-motion Strowger switch or a single-motion rotary switch, which searches for the circuit on which the calling signal originated. Used in step-by-step and rotary systems.

line switch

A single-motion rotary switch, or uniselector, in each subscriber line which rotates to find a free first selector in a certain type of step-by-step system.

link (trunk)

The connection between the terminals of one switch and the terminals on a switch of the next stage corresponding to a single transmission path.

link (one-way and two-way)

A one-way link is used only for the establishment of connections in one direction, while a two-way link is used for the establishment of connections in either direction.

link system

A system in which: (1) there are at least two connecting stages; (2) a connection is made over one or more links; (3) the links are chosen in a single logical operation; and (4) links are seized only when they can be used in making a connection.

logic function

The relationship of two or more Boolean variables as expressed by Boolean algebra.

logic gates

Electrical or electronic circuits which control the transfer of signals and produce the required outputs for specific input combinations to implement Boolean logic functions.

logic (hard-wired)

Control logic in an exchange, which is wired in circuit form.

logic (soft-wired)

Control logic in an exchange, which is held in software computer programs.

loop disconnect pulsing

Subset dial pulsing in which the subscriber DC loop is interrupted to produce pulses for signaling an exchange.

marker

Circuits which incorporate the function of busy testing, locating and finally controlling the establishment of a particular path through the switching network.

marking

The use of electrical potentials and grounds at certain points in a switching network to control its operation.

matrix

A simple switching network in which a specified inlet (matrix row) has access to a specified outlet (matrix column) via a crosspoint placed at the intersection of the row and column in question. A complete matrix is one in which each inlet has access to each outlet, while an incomplete matrix is one in which each inlet may have access to only some of the outlets.

mean delay of calls delayed

The total waiting time of all calls divided by the number of delayed calls.

message switching

A method of receiving and storing a message for a more appropriate time of retransmission. With such a method, no direct connection is established between the incoming and outgoing lines as in the case of circuit switching.

multifrequency signaling

Signaling between subscribers and the central office through a combination of audio frequencies, as with pushbutton dialing. Also, in many cases signaling between exchanges is accomplished by combinations of frequencies.

multigroup

A combination of two or more PCM multiplex channels.

occupancy

The average proportion of time that a traffic carrying facility is busy.

packet-switching

Essentially the same as message-switching.

panel switching system

A common control electromechanical switching system, which was used widely in the U.S. prior to its virtual replacement by crossbar and other systems. The banks of selectors take the form of flat vertical panels, from which the name of the system was derived. Some panel installations are still in use in the U.S.

path

A set of links joined in series to establish a connection. Paths differ if one or more links differ.

primary center

A switching center connecting toll centers, which can also serve as a toll center for its local end offices. In the U.S. it is devined as a Class 3 office.

private automatic branch exchange (PABX)

A private automatic telephone exchange which provides for the connection of calls going to and coming from the public telephone network (usually a central office exchange) as well as intra-exchange calls between the served extensions.

probability of delay

The probability that a call attempt, if offered, cannot be completed immediately.

probability of lost calls (probability of loss)

The probability that a call attempt, if offered, will be lost.

program store

The memory section of a stored program control switching system in which semi-permanent instructions and translations are contained. These are fed to the central processor to permit it to provide stored program control.

public switched network

Any switching system that provides circuit switching facilities for use by the public. Telephone, Telex, TWX, and Broadband switched networks are the public switched networks in the U.S.

pulse amplitude modulation (PAM)

A form of pulse modulation in which a number of channels are multiplexed by time sampling, but one in which the pulse amplitudes vary in accordance with the amplitude of the analog signal levels.

pulse code modulation (PCM)

A form of pulse modulation in which a number of channels are multiplexed by time sampling as in PAM, but with each amplitude replaced by a group of binary pulses which identify the amplitude of the PAM pulse which they have replaced.

pushbutton dialing

An arrangement in which the dialing function is accomplished by pushbutton control of multi-frequency signaling. AT&T refers to this type of dialing as Touch-Tone. GTE Automatic Electric calls it Touch-Call. It is also referred to as tone-dialing.

reed relay

Small sealed reed relays which are often used in the speech-path switching networks of electronically-controlled exchanges. In a broader sense, reed relays also have control circuit applications as well.

regional center

The highest level switching center in intertoll and direct distance dialing operations, designated as a Class 1 office in the U.S.

register

Pulse receiving and storage circuits in a common control exchange. In some systems it also performs limited translation functions.

register-translator

A register combined with a translator to provide the necessary information for effecting the common control of a switching system, particularly the step-by-step or Strowger type.

retiming

The process necessary to control the deviations experienced by PCM signal when it is processed at another exchange under the control of a different clock than that of the originating exchange.

revertive pulsing

Ground pulses generated by selector rods or commutators in panel and rotary selector switches. They are returned to senders or registers to effect the control of the system.

rotary switching system

Switching systems in which rotating selector and line finder switches establish the speech path through the exchange. Such systems usually utilize registers to effect a degree of common control.

scanner

The equipment used to monitor the state of calls in progress in a stored program control switching system.

sectional center

Switching Centers between the primary centers and regional centers, designated as Class 2 offices in the U.S.

select bar

The horizontal and vertical bars, which carry the select fingers and which are controlled by electromagnets in a crossbar switch to position the fingers so that the proper crosspoint contacts are made.

selecting function

The selection of the speech path by the operation of one or more two-motion Strowger selector switches in a step-by-step system. Selecting functions refer to all operations between the line finder and the output of the system, including the connector or final selector stage. Rotary and panel systems also depend upon selecting functions.

selection stage

Switching stages which contain the selector switches in a step-by-step rotary or panel system.

sender

Digit-storing and pulse-generating circuits which provide signaling information to distant exchanges from step-by-step offices.

signal distributors

Equipment which provide an interface between the high speed computer output and the low speed peripheral equipment in stored program control switching systems.

slip

In PCM systems the difference in clock speeds between the originating and terminating exchanges causes a slip in the readout from the retiming store. Thus, the signal is mutilated accordingly.

space-division switching

That type of communication switching in which distinct physical connections are switched to provide for each call, as in a crosspoint array.

step-by-step switching

The Strowger system in which two-motion switches under direct or progressive control establish speech paths in a step-by-step fashion through line finders, selectors and connector stages.

store and forward

The message or packet-switching technique in which messages are stored before transmission, which usually occurs later at a more appropriate time.

stored program control

The form of control applied in electronic switching systems to permit the storage of the necessary common control information in a software form, which can be readily changed to provide for new services and accommodate new requirements.

Strowger switching system

The switching system which utilizes two-motion selector and connector switches named for the inventor of the first step-by-step system—Almon B. Strowger.

subset

The subscriber's telephone instrument.

switching algebra

The application of Boolean algebra to the analysis of switching circuits as first proposed by Claude B. Shannon of Bell Telephone Laboratories.

switch block

Groups of switching elements, usually arranged in matrix-like arrays.

switching network (homogeneous and heterogeneous)

An arrangement of switches whose function is to connect inlets to outlets. Generally several connections exist simultaneously through a switching network. A homogeneous switching network is one in which every connection between an inlet and outlet uses the same number of crosspoints. A heterogeneous switching network is one in which different connections between inlets and outlets may use different numbers of crosspoints.

switching stage

Those switches in a switching network which have identical parallel functions. A switching stage is composed of switch blocks.

synchronous system

A system in which the originating and terminating exchanges are operated continuously at the same frequency. Such in-phase operation is maintained by corrective means, if necessary.

tandem office

An exchange to interconnect local central offices over tandem trunks in densely settled exchange areas, where it is not economical to provide direct connections between all central offices.

tariff

The rate for equipment, facilities, or types of servicrs as provided by common communications carriers.

Telex

A dial-up telegraph service available to subscribers to communicate directly between themselves through circuits of the public telegraph network. Worldwide service with Baudot code is provided.

time-division switching

That type of communication in which voice channels are separated in time and are not switched through distinct physical connections as contrasted with space-division switching. With such switching systems digital data may be switched in its original form.

time sampling

> The process, in pulse modulation, where a series of short pulses of current or voltage are produced so that their amplitudes correspond to the characteristic ordinates in the original signal waveform.

toll center

> An exchange where outgoing circuits from local central and tandem offices and toll message circuits are brought together. It is designated as a Class 4 office in the U.S.

Touch-Calling (Touch-Tone)

> Touch-Calling and Touch-Tone are the proprietary terms of GTE Automatic Electric and AT&T, respectively, for pushbutton dialing.

traffic capacity

> The traffic volume occurring during a specified period of time divided by the duration of the period; both quantities being expressed in the same unit of time. The unit of measurement is the erlang.

traffic intensity

> The traffic intensity which can be handled by a given group of switching devices for a prescribed value of some congestion function.

translation

> The conversion of information in one code to another as in the conversion of directory number (DN) information to equipment number (EN) information or vice versa. Such conversions are necessary to provide flexibility within exchanges as well as between exchanges. In the latter case signaling information between exchanges may require a different code than that furnished by subscribers to the originating exchange.

trunk

A circuit connecting exchanges. Examples are interoffice and intertoll trunks.

twistor

A magnetic storage device used in the program store of No. 1 and No. 2 ESS stored program control switching systems. In this application it is used in a card-changeable mechanically alterable store. Another version of the twistor, known as a piggyback twistor, makes possible an electrically-alterable store. It is used in TSPS and in the SP-1 system of Northern Electric. See text for detailed explanation of their operation. In the above applications a nondestructive readout is provided.

TWX (Teletypewriter exchange service)

A public switched teletype service in which suitably arranged teletypewriter stations are provided with lines to a central office for access to stations throughout the U.S. and Canada. Both Baudot and ASCII-coded teletype machines are used. This system was operated by AT&T until it was acquired by Western Union, who now operates it as well as the Telex service.

uniselector

A single-motion rotary switch used in step-by-step and rotary switching systems.

Venn diagram

A graphical method to portray Boolean logic functions.

waiting time (average delay)

The total waiting time of all calls divided by the number of calls offered, including those not delayed. It is equal to the mean delay of calls delayed multiplied by the probability of delay.

wander

A timing variation in PCM transmission with a long time constant.

Appendix
Symbology and Nomenclature

Throughout this book a variety of symbols has been used in the diagraming of switching systems, their subsystems and components. This variation is due to the use of different symbols and to some extent different nomenclature by the several equipment manufacturers and developers, and due to the lack of standardization in the field.

In Chapter 5, the symbology of the British engineer T.H. Flowers, was adopted to diagram the general functions of communications switching systems, because it illustrates the fundamental concepts of receiving, processing, and transmitting of signaling information. These concepts are of key significance in understanding exchange switching. However, there are other approaches to the classification and unification of switching system functions. In this Appendix a proposal of A.E. Joel, Jr., of Bell Telephone Laboratories is presented. In this proposal it is contended that if the industry is to make progress in understanding principles and finding the bases for comparing and evaluating switching systems of the future, more sophisticated analytical methods are needed. It is proposed that certain functions be recognized as fundamental in the design of telecommunications switching and that when such functions are agreed upon, they be utilized to provide high-level descriptions of switching systems.

A specific set of switching system functions are outlined in this proposal and their application to electromechanical and electronic switching systems is illustrated. These specific functions are: (1) call signal processing, (2) call information processing, and (3) switching networks and their controls. In this proposal call signal processing (CSP) includes the receipt, registering or storage, and transmission of signals by the exchange. The signals consist of service requests, digital information of calling and called addresses, and call supervision. Call information processing (CIP) involves the actions necessary to interpret, convert, and control the internal flow of call information and make decisions based on it. Such information includes the calling and called addresses and the use of translation data relative to these addresses.

Switching networks and their controls are divided into the switching center network and access networks. Each such network has an abbreviated letter designation and the control function for each network is designated NC. The following switching networks are defined:

1. The switching center (designated SCN) is the principle network of the exchange and is used to interconnect lines or trunks to each other. This network may have several separate subdivisions—such as for switching lines to outgoing trunks or incoming trunks to lines.

2. Access networks (AN) are used in register and common-control systems and are subdivided into signal access networks (SAN) and control access networks (CAN). The latter is in turn subdivided into network control access networks (NCAN) and intracontrol access networks (ICAN). The signal access networks (SANs) are used to connect the call signal processing portion of a system to the lines and trunks. Space-division SANs usually pass information in two directions in register, sender, and service-circuit links. Time-division SANs pass information in only one direction in scanners and signal distributors. Control access network (CAN) subclasses are: (a) network control access networks (NCAN), which are used to connect the inputs, outputs, or links of any network being controlled to the network controls; and (b) intracontrol access networks (ICAN), which are used to provide paths for the flow of information between control functions.

THE APPLICATION OF PROPOSED SYMBOLOGY AND NOMENCLATURE

A progressive direct control system of the line finder type is shown in Fig. A-1. Here the line circuit is a call signal processing (CSP) circuit, which detects service requests. The line finder switch (SCN) is controlled by its own control (NC) through the allotter (CAN). The selector switches (SCN) are controlled directly by a call signal processing (CSP) circuit of each selector stage. An indirect control progressive system is shown in Fig. A-2. Here the register-senders are the call signal

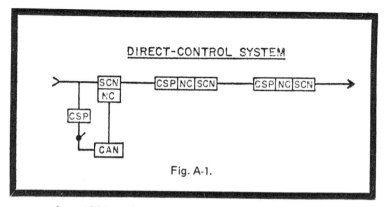

Fig. A-1.

processing (CSP) elements. As shown by the dotted lines, there may be either an individual translator (CIP) as in the step-by-step director system, or a common translator working through a control access network (CAN).

The application of this symbology and nomenclature to the No. 5 Crossbar system is shown in Fig. A-3. In this case the network control and the call information processing functions are integrated. Although No. 5 Crossbar uses separate dial tone and completing markers, they are shown here as one marker (CIP1) for simplicity. A separate common translator (CIP2) is also used in this system. The outgoing senders are connected to the outgoing trunks. The originating register is accessed directly through the switching center network (SCN). After call registration, the line is reconnected to the appropriate type of trunk (a call signal processing function).

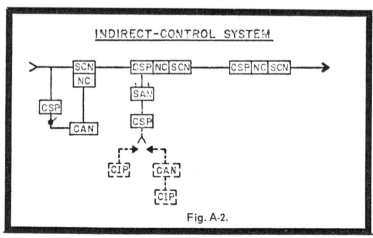

Fig. A-2.

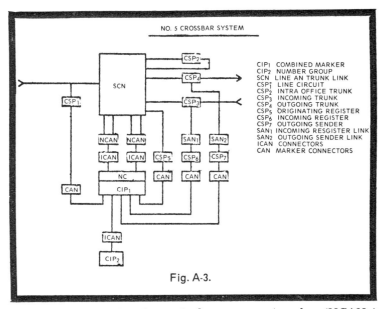

NO. 5 CROSSBAR SYSTEM

CIP₁	COMBINED MARKER
CIP₂	NUMBER GROUP
SCN	LINE AN TRUNK LINK
CSP₁	LINE CIRCUIT
CSP₂	INTRA OFFICE TRUNK
CSP₃	INCOMING TRUNK
CSP₄	OUTGOING TRUNK
CSP₅	ORIGINATING REGISTER
CSP₆	INCOMING REGISTER
CSP₇	OUTGOING SENDER
SAN₁	INCOMING RESGISTER LINK
SAN₂	OUTGOING SENDER LINK
ICAN	CONNECTORS
CAN	MARKER CONNECTORS

Fig. A-3.

Two separate network control access networks (NCANs) access the four stages of the switching center network (SCN) for control purposes.

The No. 1 ESS, shown in Fig. A-4, is of the divided switching center network type. Here one-way electronic networks called scanners and signal distributors perform the signal access network (SAN) functions. A call information

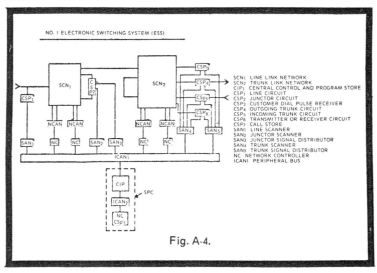

NO. 1 ELECTRONIC SWITCHING SYSTEM (ESS)

SCN₁	LINE LINK NETWORK
SCN₂	TRUNK LINK NETWORK
CIP₁	CENTRAL CONTROL AND PROGRAM STORE
CSP₁	LINE CIRCUIT
CSP₂	JUNCTOR CIRCUIT
CSP₃	CUSTOMER DIAL PULSE RECEIVER
CSP₄	OUTGOING TRUNK CIRCUIT
CSP₅	INCOMING TRUNK CIRCUIT
CSP₆	TRANSMITTER OR RECEIVER CIRCUIT
CSP₇	CALL STORE
SAN₁	LINE SCANNER
SAN₂	JUNCTOR SCANNER
SAN₃	JUNCTOR SIGNAL DISTRIBUTOR
SAN₄	TRUNK SCANNER
SAN₅	TRUNK SIGNAL DISTRIBUTOR
NC	NETWORK CONTROLLER
ICAN1	PERIPHERAL BUS

Fig. A-4.

processing (CIP) function and its access in this case to combined call signal processing-network control (CSP∕NC) are brought together by the stored program control (SPC). The CSP∕NC functions are implemented in effect in call stores which carry signal information and a network map in their memories. Communications functions peripheral to the stored program control are provided by high-speed electronic buses. The bus access is an intracontrol access network and is designated as an ICAN.

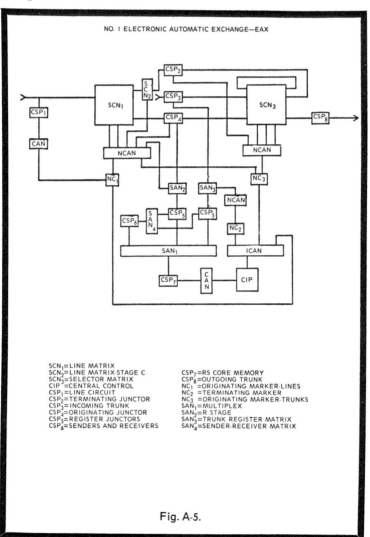

NO. 1 ELECTRONIC AUTOMATIC EXCHANGE—EAX

SCN₁=LINE MATRIX
SCN₂=LINE MATRIX-STAGE C
SCN₃=SELECTOR MATRIX
CIP =CENTRAL CONTROL
CSP₁=LINE CIRCUIT
CSP₂=TERMINATING JUNCTOR
CSP₃=INCOMING TRUNK
CSP₄=ORIGINATING JUNCTOR
CSP₅=REGISTER JUNCTORS
CSP₆=SENDERS AND RECEIVERS

CSP₇=RS CORE MEMORY
CSP₈=OUTGOING TRUNK
NC₁ =ORIGINATING MARKER-LINES
NC₂ =TERMINATING MARKER
NC₃ =ORIGINATING MARKER-TRUNKS
SAN₁=MULTIPLEX
SAN₂=R STAGE
SAN₃=TRUNK REGISTER MATRIX
SAN₄=SENDER-RECEIVER MATRIX

Fig. A-5.

In Fig. A-5, Automatic Electric's No. 1 EAX system is shown. Although in a broad basic sense it resembles No. 1 ESS, it includes the signal access network (SAN) for controlling the call signal processing (CSP) junctor circuits. Also, a switching control network (SCN2) is added for intraoffice calls.

Index